The Long Crossing and Other Labrador Stories

For Eileen Furth
with all good wishes from
Elliott Merrick

BOOKS BY ELLIOTT MERRICK

True North

Northern Nurse

Frost and Fire

Ever the Winds Blow

From This Hill Look Down

Green Mountain Farm

Passing By

The Long Crossing and Other Labrador Stories

THE LONG CROSSING

and Other Labrador Stories

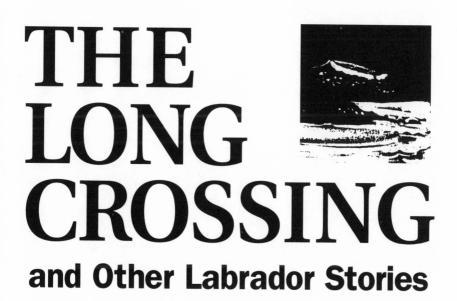

Elliott Merrick

With an Introduction by
Ronald Rompkey

University of Maine Press

© 1992 by Elliott Merrick
Published by the University of Maine Press
51 Public Affairs Building, Orono, Maine 04469 U.S.A

92 94 96 98 00 02 01 99 97 95 93
1 2 3 4

"*Kyle* Comes to Indian Harbour" was originally published in the International Grenfell Association magazine, *Among the Deep Sea Fishers*. "Passing the Time" is a chapter in the book *Northern Nurse* (Charles Scribner's Sons, 1942; reprinted 1982, Sherry Urie). Used by permission. "Snowshoe Trail" was first published in *Scribner's Magazine*, December 1932. "He Sailed Away" was first published in the magazine *Story*, December 1942. "The Lone Wolf" was published in *Scribner's Magazine*, March 1938. "Without Words" first appeared in *Scribner's Magazine*, January 1938. "Mina Paddon and the Winter of the Flu" is reprinted with permission from the *Newfoundland Quarterly* 80, no. 4 (1985).

Library of Congress Cataloging-in-Publication Data

Merrick, Elliott, 1905–
   The long crossing and other Labrador stories / Elliott Merrick ;
with an introduction by Ronald Rompkey.
      p.   cm.
ISBN 0-89101-074-2
   1. Labrador (Nfld.)   2. Labrador (Nfld.)—Fiction.   I. Title.
F1136.M35   1991
971.8'2—dc20   91-32226
                                                  CIP

Manufactured in the United States of America

CONTENTS

MAPS

PREFACE

I AM GRATEFUL to Professor Ronald Rompkey for interesting the University of Maine Press in publishing this book of short stories. He has been an enthusiastic promoter of this project from the start, and I will always be appreciative of his efforts in my behalf.

I first learned of the three canoe-and-portage expeditions recounted in "The Long Crossing" in 1930, when I was living in North West River. One afternoon I paddled across the river to visit Bert Blake, whom I admired greatly. He was at that time a famous guide and wilderness traveler, spending summers guiding prospectors on long canoe trips to the sites of the present-day iron mines in the middle of Labrador. From the loft of his house that day he brought down a book and showed it to me. It was Mina Hubbard's *A Woman's Way through Unknown Labrador,* which she had inscribed and sent to him.

Many years before, at sixteen years of age, Bert Blake had made the long crossing of Labrador as camp cook and one of Mrs. Hubbard's guides. Now, in 1930, Blake was a man of action and not impressed by books. I, however, was fascinated with Mrs. Hubbard's narrative.

In subsequent years I discovered that a number of accounts have been written about the death of Leonidas Hubbard and the three Hubbard-Wallace expeditions. The participants themselves published three separate books. These accounts emphasized the point of view of one or the other of the participants, or focused on some special aspect of the expeditions.

It seemed to me there was more to the story. I wanted to put the three different expeditions into one unified, chronological narrative that would convey the whole story for readers who had never before heard of the Hubbards and Dillon Wallace. I wanted to connect, in a close-knit pattern, those three attempts to cross the Labrador wilderness, just as they were in reality related.

By the time my own account was written, Mrs. Hubbard had remarried and was an elderly woman living in a London hotel. She kindly read my draft and wrote from England that she approved my version of those long ago life-and-death events.

As for the other stories, they are all the outgrowth of personal experience, the travels and the people I knew long ago. Returning in later years, I found, of course, that the old days are no more. Conditions and traditions changed little in past centuries, but ways of life in the north have altered almost beyond recognition in the relatively short period since World War II. Snowmobiles take the place of snowshoes and toboggans. Dogteams are rare or nonexistent. Indians no longer fashion canoes by hand. The upper flow of the Naskaupi River has been diverted. The Grand Falls have been harnessed, and the Smallwood and Ossokmanuan reservoirs now cover land where many of the events recounted here took place. However, much of that vast wilderness remains lonely and untouched.

I am fortunate to have known the strong, courageous, capable men and women who lived in that land sixty years ago. These are the people of my stories.

Elliott Merrick

INTRODUCTION

THIS VOLUME reintroduces Elliott Merrick, a writer of the
1930s and 1940s who speaks to the contemporary reader with all
his original power. Best known as a wilderness writer and recog-
nized for Labrador books such as *True North* and *Northern Nurse*,
he has written over the years a variety of shorter pieces extolling
human individuality and independence, the best of them also set
in Labrador. They concern themselves with the community of
Scottish and Inuit settlers established around Hamilton Inlet who
have traditionally supplied furs to the Hudson's Bay Company. In
his earliest Labrador publication, "Escape to the North," Merrick
described this community as a "unique race" sprung from an odd
combination of cultures: "Scotch Presbyterian in religion, old
English in speech and many customs, Eskimo when it comes to
seal fishing and dog driving, Indian in their ways of hunting and
their skill with canoes ascending the big rivers bound for the trapping grounds in the country." As a young traveler, Merrick developed a strong affinity for these people and for what he perceived
as their blend of hardihood, cheer, courage, enterprise, intelli-
gence, and kindness, and framed his narratives around them. How
did such a liaison come about?

Merrick was born in Montclair, New Jersey, the son of Elliott
Tucker Merrick, Jr., and Margaret Day Merrick on May 11, 1905.
Comfortably placed in a highly stratified town, he watched his
father commute daily to New York City, where he was president of
Hoyt Metal, a branch of the National Lead Company. The family

spent their summers at a rented cottage in Ogunquit, Maine, getting up tennis tournaments, swimming, mixing with their fellow
vacationers from New York, Philadelphia, and Chicago, and chum-
ming with local fishermen in nearby Perkins Cove. Merrick discovered early a passion for boats, but at the age of sixteen he discovered something else: he liked writing even better than boating.
After two years at Montclair High School, he was sent by his father
to Phillips Exeter Academy, a "stern, joyless school" as he described
it, but one that taught him to study and provided him with an avenue to Yale.

After the rigors of Phillips Exeter, Merrick entered Yale in 1923 to
study English literature and French. At the same time, he joined
Beta Theta Pi, played hockey and tennis competitively and acted
as New Haven correspondent for the *New York Evening Post*. He
was introduced to the mainstreams of English and American literature by such professors as William Lyon Phelps, Chauncey Tinker,
and Stanley Williams, but he remembered most vividly a modest
course called Daily Themes, an introduction to writing taught by
John Berdan. Here Berdan laid the foundations of a spare, under-
stated style and cultivated in Merrick the knack of allowing a story
to "tell itself" through daily exercises that forced him to see events
as a writer. Still, he had no idea how he would earn a living doing
this, and when his proud father raised the matter at his Yale graduation, Merrick told him he still wasn't sure. One thing he was sure
of: he did not want to enter the world of business.

Determined to pursue an apprenticeship through journalism,
he next spent a year reporting routine meetings and covering
funerals for the Passaic Daily News and another six months editing
the weekly *Pompton Lakes Journal*. The narrow scope of these New
Jersey papers soon bored him, however, and when he was offered a
job as an assistant advertising manager in the New York offices of
the National Lead Company, he took it. For nearly a year, he turned
out copy for Dutch Boy White Lead Paint and the U.S. Cartridge
Company, commuting daily by train as he had vowed he never
would. As soon as he had saved two thousand dollars, he quit, seeing his chance to write his first book. Retiring to a cottage on the
Rhode Island shore, he wrote a biography of the mountain climber
Henri Russell, whom he regarded as a kind of French Thoreau, but
could find no publisher to accept it. Frustrated, he signed himself
on as a deckhand aboard an American Export Lines freighter

bound around the world. After a week of cleaning rotten Egyptian onions out of its hold by day and watching a colony of bedbugs map fresh trails across his abdomen by night, he concluded that this was not the kind of romance he sought and left the vessel behind, having ventured no further than the Brooklyn docks. Without the freighter and its crew of malcontents, he would later conjecture, he might never have known anything about Labrador or Wilfred Grenfell.

IF WILFRED GRENFELL did not discover Labrador, he had become by then its unrivaled promoter and benefactor. In 1891, concerned citizens in St. John's, Newfoundland, had responded to tales of extreme poverty and starvation on the Labrador coast with a call to the National Mission to Deep Sea Fishermen, a British society that since 1882 had acted as a virtual police force in the North Sea in the continuing campaign to rid English fishermen of the Dutch "copers," grog ships that plied the fishing grounds and sold cheap liquor. An evangelical body with no direct church affiliation, the mission had pioneered medical care in the fishing industry, first by sending doctors aboard the fishing smacks and then by designing hospital ships that could be kept at sea. By supplying reading material, knitted clothing, regular worship, and medical care for lonely fishermen afloat for weeks on end, it had assisted in eliminating the copers altogether. Wilfred Grenfell, freshly trained at the London Hospital Medical School, became the mission's doctor in 1888 and ultimately its first superintendent. It was Grenfell who supervised the medical team sent to Labrador in the spring of 1892 and who dedicated the rest of his life to improving the lives of the inhabitants by building hospitals and nursing stations and then by attempting to reform the social system through the introduction of cooperative stores, schools, home industries, and other innovations. To finance these costly ventures, he undertook lecture tours throughout North America to bring in the needed cash and attract young volunteers.

Raised as an evangelical Anglican, Grenfell had been inspired by the American revivalist Dwight L. Moody during his early medical training and had practiced a religious liberalism bordering on Unitarianism. In his subsequent preaching and publishing, he had eschewed ritual and dogma and had instead called for a religious life of virtuous action, a practical sense of Christian duty that

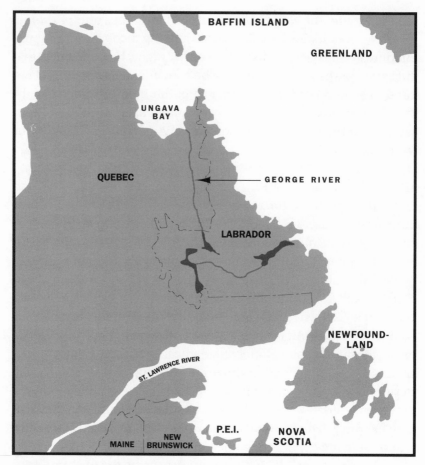

Map 1 Labrador shown in relation to adjacent areas of Canada.

appealed to many middle-class Protestants. Aside from the professional doctors, nurses, and teachers who served in northern
Newfoundland and Labrador, Grenfell attracted in those days hundreds of young students looking for interesting and useful occupa-
tion and willing to work without pay. Chiefly Americans, they
taught in the schools, assisted at the hospitals, ran the boats, dug
the ditches, built the residences, put in the plumbing, and sometimes returned in later years as qualified nurses, dentists, and
medical doctors to run the mission. Once home in Canada, the
United States, or Britain, they also organized sales, gave lectures,
and brought in other volunteers. In 1914, Grenfell formed his own
international mission, and by 1926 the Grenfell organization was
supported almost completely by American funds and American

personnel. That year, Grenfell found it necessary to organize an overseas branch of his own burgeoning organization, the Grenfell Association of Great Britain and Ireland, to encourage donations and volunteers.

It was 1929 when Elliott Merrick discharged himself from the freighter in Brooklyn, still looking for adventure in some remote place, and with the summer still in hand he agreed to serve as a volunteer at the Grenfell station in Indian Harbour. Here he met Grenfell, the resourceful and robust evangelical he admired, and was surprised by the man's aura of British authority and dignity. Even more, he was attracted by Labrador and its people, and at the end of the summer he decided to stay on as a teacher of the third and fourth grades at the mission school in North West River, a fur trading center with a medical station administered by Dr. Harry Paddon and his wife, Mina, a nurse. Paddon, who had been inspired by Grenfell's enthusiasm while still a schoolboy at Repton, was one of the extraordinarily tenacious laborers in the Grenfell vineyard. As a medical student at St. Thomas's Hospital, he like Grenfell had served the Mission to Deep Sea Fishermen in the North Sea, allowing himself fifteen months at the Guest Hospital in Dudley before joining the Labrador branch full time in 1912. The Paddons influenced Merrick's life directly. But even more dramatically, Merrick fell in love with Paddon's resident Australian nurse, Kate Austen, and married her. It was she who continued to be the faithful moral supporter of his writing career throughout the ensuing decades until her death in 1989.

AFTER TWO YEARS at North West River, including a spell as a trapper, Merrick found he could not make a living, even though Labrador satisfied his desire for simplicity and hard work. In 1931, the two returned to the United States to find that with the Great Depression well advanced, no better opportunities awaited them there. When Merrick departed from New York, he had left his two thousand dollars on margin with a stockbroker with orders to sell as soon as it had doubled. But by now he had lost all of it, and he owed the broker a fee. With no job at hand, he started writing again and produced "Escape to the North." And when this first effort was quickly picked up by *Scribner's Magazine*, he began to feel that his life had changed. Unknown to Merrick, since 1928 *Scribner's* had struggled to rid itself of its stodginess with lively alterations in content and format so as to propel itself back into the midst of the magazine market, aiming at a public lying somewhere between its former self and the improved *Saturday Evening Post.* Wilderness writing fitted in with their plan, and Merrick left the Scribner offices on Fifth Avenue with two hundred dollars in his pocket.

At this important juncture, he had made a serious decision to write. There followed "Snowshoe Trail" in *Scribner's Magazine* and his first book, *True North* (1933), which Scribner also published. In this volume, he produced one of the romantically definitive descriptions of Labrador life, recounting the experiences of Kay and himself during a canoe-and-portage journey with trappers three hundred miles up the Churchill River and back, capturing as no one has since the joy of strenuousness and survival in the Labrador wilderness. The book conveyed a strong Thoreauvian simplicity and independence epitomized in this short manifesto:

> Each man has only one lifetime, and in that space he gets what he wants most; not what he thinks he wants or would like to want, but what he really wants. Do I want a superfluity of material comforts and possessions, a dwelling loaded with conveniences, foods from all over the world, the power to ride and not walk, electric lights, good clothes, cement sidewalks, water out of a faucet, public parks and all that? Are they worth what they cost? Do I want to bend my whole life to a system of law, convention, taboo, evolved solely to enable millions of people to live packed together like sardines in a can? Hardly.

Merrick's hardy romanticism in *True North* struck home to the urban reader. The *New York Times Book Review* drew links with Rousseau, Chateaubriand, and Thoreau. "It has in it, too, a courageous realism and a vividness that makes one go to the window of a Manhattan apartment on a mild February night and find with some surprise that the snow is not piled deep, nor the horizon bounded by spruce-clad hills, nor the air crackling with a fifty-below-zero temperature," wrote the reviewer.

By now the Merricks were renting an abandoned subsistence farm in Vermont for five dollars a month and working it while they started a family. During these years, recounted in a small book-of-days, *From This Hill Look Down* (1934), and later in

Green Mountain Farm (1948), Merrick would change into his "city" clothes once or twice a year and venture into New York to confer with Scribner editor Maxwell Perkins at Perkins's accustomed lunching place, an Italian restaurant on 53rd Street. Here, Perkins would sit with his hat perched on his head and order his usual mid-day martini while he spoke of other Scribner authors like Hemingway, Fitzgerald, and Thomas Wolfe and their current problems. Merrick found the practice exotic, but he regarded Perkins with reverence. At the time, Perkins was preeminent among editors and devoted to his authors. As one observer wrote, the encouragement of talent was to him a "sacred task" worth any amount of effort.

Ever alert to the inventive and the experimental in new fiction, Perkins responded strongly to Merrick's evocation of Labrador life and encouraged him to continue. At a time when publishing still maintained the style of a gentlemanly art rather than a business, Merrick thought Perkins took a risk with him. He agreed to publish the fictional autobiography *Ever the Winds Blow* (1936). He also published the Labrador novel *Frost and Fire* (1939), and three more stories, including "Without Words." (The latter, Merrick's most widely circulated literary production, was reprinted more than fifty times, published in England, translated into Danish, and included in a Bantam anthology that sold more than a million copies.)

During the ten years in Vermont, while Merrick turned his literary attention to farm life, Labrador intruded again. To supplement his income from writing and farming, he was teaching at the high school in Craftsbury Common and coaching the hockey team. From 1939, he taught English at the University of Vermont, and Kay sometimes addressed clubs and organizations about the medical work of the Grenfell mission. The vividness of her reminiscences led Merrick to write *Northern Nurse* (1942), his most successful book commercially. With this volume, the two collaborated so as to produce a book about frontier medicine that would engage the lay reader. Local characters appeared and reappeared, and the hospital in Hamilton Inlet, the problems, the people, the bay took on a life of their own. Perkins liked it so much he said he did not wish to change a line, and it was enthusiastically reviewed in the metropolitan dailies as well as the *Saturday Review of Literature* and *Publishers Weekly*. It stayed on the *New York Times* bestseller list for seventeen weeks. Nevertheless, with the publishing market in disarray, the acclaim still did not permit Merrick to write full time.

With the attack on Pearl Harbor, war intervened, and he attempted to join the United States Navy. At the same time, other misfortunes curtailed book sales. Dorothy Canfield Fisher, an influential judge of the Book-of-the-Month Club, admired "Without Words" and wanted to make *Northern Nurse* a Book of the Month, but she could not gather enough support. *Reader's Digest* paid $500 for a one-year option on *Northern Nurse* as a condensed book but after a year declined to take it up. A proposal to make a film of *Frost and Fire* was floated and then dropped. Rejected by the navy for a touch of color blindness, Merrick employed his pen at the Office of War Information in Washington and New York, working under Henry Pringle, a winner of the Pulitzer Prize for his biography of Theodore Roosevelt. After Berdan and Perkins, Pringle became Merrick's third teacher, urging him through repeated drafts of a booklet on the United Nations and a variety of propaganda pamphlets aimed at encouraging the Resistance. His booklet on the United Nations Merchant Marine, reinforcing the need for a lifeline to Europe during the protracted Battle of the Atlantic, emerged as his most widely read production after it was translated into sundry European languages and dropped by the million into the occupied countries. On the other hand, his "Sicilian friendship book" quickly became redundant when the liberating armies encountered Sicilian citizens brimming with good will, most of them claiming kinship with residents of New York City.

With the war over, the University of Vermont insisted that Merrick pursue a Ph.D. if he wanted to maintain his academic status. Citing his collection of books, he resisted and after an extended struggle with the administration he left disenchanted. He moved into another teaching position at Black Mountain College, North Carolina, a more hospitable institution with an appealing setting in the wooded Southern Appalachians and a more flexible attitude to academic freedom. Hired as an associate professor, Merrick for a year taught creative writing and English to returning G.I.'s ready to make up for lost time and began to enjoy himself again. But when the U.S. Department of Agriculture offered him a research editorship at the Southeastern Forest Experiment Station in Asheville, headquarters for forest research in five states, he was ready to move on again. By this time, his three children were growing up, and he wanted them to go to college. The task of making science clear to lay readers while at the same time teaching foresters the craft of writing offered him a new challenge and a measure of the cherished independence he craved. Here he stayed for twenty-two years.

Meanwhile, two more books were developing. Working in Washington on a merchant navy booklet, he had carefully observed the war's effect on private lives. During the winter of 1944–45, he had managed to sign on aboard a convoy tanker bound for England and from this experience produced *Passing By* (1947), an exploration of the varieties of separation imposed on men and women. The men of the merchant service, as Merrick portrayed them, were a rowdy, hard-drinking species who had volunteered to go to sea in hazardous circumstances. They displayed, thought Merrick, a kind of heroism too often overshadowed by the exploits of their naval counterparts, who were better equipped to fight back from the relative safety of their escort vessels. Sadly, the book brought about his departure from Scribner's.

Scribner's still clung to its Victorian conservatism. Charles Scribner, president of the firm, forbade profanity in his books, and Maxwell Perkins was so prudish that he could not bring himself to utter common four-letter words. When pressed by editorial duty, he preferred to write them down. He had succeeded in holding on against encroaching profanity and sexual explicitness before, notably with *The Sun Also Rises* (1926), *A Farewell to Arms* (1929), and the early submissions of Marjorie Kinnan Rawlings. In addition, Merrick claims Perkins was not "himself" in those days. In fact, his health deteriorated markedly in 1944, and he died in 1947. Even though *Passing By* had been twice rewritten for him, he continued to reject it as he had rejected other promising books. But confident of its value, Merrick took it to Macmillan, where it soon came out and paid its way. Similarly, Macmillan took up *Green Mountain Farm* (1948), Merrick's paean to the rustic life. Merrick would not publish with Scribner again.

THE LONG CROSSING and Other Labrador Stories is the first collection of Merrick's short pieces. It begins with four nonfiction stories, two of them autobiographical and one ("Isle of Demons," a sketch of Belle Isle lighthouse keepers) published here for the first time. Three fictional pieces follow, "He Sailed Away," "The Lone

Wolf," and "Without Words." The final two selections return to nonfiction, and the last, "The Long Crossing," is also published here for the first time.

These pieces draw from a literary tradition in which "nature," as opposed to the customary, the artificial, and the conventional, serves as a norm for human behavior, and they reestablish Elliott Merrick as a significant exponent of that tradition. A generation ago, Merrick himself made a rare critical reference to his romantic assumptions in his Yale class history when he wrote, "Through most of [my stories] weaves the thread that 'man is great but nature is greater,' and that the function of a highly developed civilization should be to lead men closer to the heart of the world, not farther away." There is something of Thoreau's idealism in writing like this, without Thoreau's condescension and his tendency to lecture. Rather, it draws upon a nonrealistic tradition in which stories become embodiments of human desire or aspiration set against the immanent power of the landscape. As a contemporary reviewer once observed, Merrick arrives at a critical point of American reference, "the point at which the Calvinist idea of salvation by individual works had been incongruously grafted to the Rousseauist doctrine of nature as the blameless mother of mankind." Whatever one may think of that observation, one may at least see the outlines of two romantic features in his work overlapping: the natives and settlers of Labrador are portrayed happily going about their accustomed tasks in accordance with their code of hard work and independence; the outsiders from the urban world—the missionaries, doctors, nurses, explorers—intrude in search of something.

By isolating himself in Labrador at a time of early introspection, Merrick himself lived something of the life of the romantic American hero and developed a personal vision that he would draw on later. Thus, some of these stories present solitary figures separated from the mainstream or rejected by it. They work out their difficulties in a place that is both remote and picturesque. Merrick assumes the persona of the poet-as-prophet, one who is acting as spokesman for certain values and attitudes of his generation at a time of crisis or discontent while looking ahead to a time of renewal. To a great extent, these figures are evocations of his own experience.

Merrick's work manifests other romantic features and values as well. It shares the assumption that whatever human beings have added by way of the arts and sciences to the "natural" condition of the race have not necessarily improved it but that, in fact, human life may be better satisfied with the fewest needs and the simplest pursuits. In "Snowshoe Trail," for example, a hunter goes snow-blind and curses his sunglasses, observing, "My glasses were fancy things from the States with sides in them and fur to go against the face. Of course they steamed up from the warmth of my face inside and the cold outside." He later learns that the "glasses" the Inuit have used for centuries, pieces of wood an inch thick with black-ened, V-shaped pinholes, would have served him much better. In "Isle of Demons," a lighthouse keeper works with an old Ford truck that gradually falls apart, until one day it nearly goes over a cliff when the brakes fail.

Other associated motifs suggested themselves. The tradition holds up for admiration manifestations of the "noble savage," men like George Elson, the part-Indian guide of "The Long Crossing," or the silent yet expressive Indian of "Without Words." These, we are shown, possess a higher form of knowledge, a shrewdness and an ingenuity that defeat and baffle more learned men like Parson Worthington in "He Sailed Away," an outsider who brings a dictio-nary to the North to help civilize the Inuit. Similarly, in "Isle of Demons," the lighthouse keeper's children study happily in their mother's elaborate substitute for a real school but learn other important lessons from the solitary existence offered by their island.

During his tenure as Labrador's principal advocate, Grenfell was often asked why it was not better to evacuate the desolate wastes and devote the costs of medical care and rural development to more productive ends. Grenfell's answer was always the same. Rather than promote short-term political gain, he preferred to see the people of Labrador as a race apart and their country a place of rich potential to which the world would beat a path. Today, many of Grenfell's dreams have already been accomplished. Minerals have been extracted, water power harnessed and open spaces traced out in grids for the training of jet fighters. The people of Labrador no longer feel the luxury of remoteness. They must make the difficult choice between inviting the world in or clinging to their cherished way of life.

But Merrick's Labrador is a place where the jet fighter and the snowmobile have not yet arrived. Snowshoe, dog team, and sail still govern the rituals of daily life, and people are left to their own devices. There persists in his landscape a sense of primitive purity, of life lived in accordance with a presumed law of nature, the urban pastoralist's equivalent of the faraway Fortunate Island or Earthly Paradise. His stories remove readers from the routine of the present just as Merrick once removed himself from the world of affairs. They bring us into contact with people, fictional and real, who are stretched to the limits of civilized behavior and brought into touch with themselves, inducing us to look more intently at those who have chosen to live at the margins of industrial society. In their distinctive way, such people deliberately place a value on what human beings are capable of, once let loose from the conventions of modern living, and they bring us a little closer to "the heart of the world."

Ronald Rompkey

The Long Crossing and Other Labrador Stories

KYLE COMES TO
INDIAN HARBOUR

I N THOSE DAYS, twenty thousand men fished for cod in summer along the Labrador. Indian Harbour Hospital, halfway "down along," was the most northerly medical establishment on the Atlantic coast. This Grenfell Mission station had been built to serve fishermen, their main affliction being dreadful infections caused by fish hooks, fish-cleaning knives, fishbones, and the chafing of oilskins on wrists.

That summer I was a "wop" at the hospital, meaning volunteer With Out Pay. We two wops, Tom and I, were men-of-all-work, among whose duties was the job of watching for the steamer. Every two weeks or so, this salt-caked messenger from away south in St. John's, Newfoundland, anchored briefly in our harbor, with mail, freight and patients who had been collected for us along the coast. We also had patients to be sent south to better-equipped establishments. Because we had no radio to give us word of her whereabouts, and because her skipper was always in a hurry, we had to have some warning of the ship's arrival if everything was to be ready and our motorboat cranked up.

For all these reasons, I found myself one wide and beautiful afternoon up on the Indian Head's bare rock forehead. The spun-yard clouds were adrift in the serene sky, the white icebergs adrift in the blue sea. Miles and miles out toward the Bear Islands a huge ice palace the size of a city block, all gleaming turrets and silver pinnacles, drifted south. A mere speck, a schooner was beating north against the breeze. In the other direction, George Island rose dripping from the water twenty miles away; and nearer, close below, fishermen in their punts were jigging cod along the sun's path. Right below my feet were the hospital roof and the harbor, where nine schooners lay at anchor. It was nearly always peaceful and blessed up on the Indian Head. Many times after a week of dirty weather, when that squat, ugly, beautiful hospital bed had been a besieged fort, warm and homely within, lashed without by rain and hail, beaten and rocked by the spray winds and wrapped close around with fog, we got downhearted and unfree. The air in the little ward where the fishermen lay in rows was heavy with pain, the pain of a clogged heart or a broken leg, but mostly the pain of sepsis—swollen fingers and bloated hands, and arms with the bright red streaks and the bulging armpits. Not their moaning and teeth-gritting and silence, not their living or their dying, but just their lying, big-eyed, in a bed got oppressive, so that Tom and I would draw lots to see who would go in there with an armful of wood for the greedy stove. Whoever lost went on tiptoe.

Maybe somebody had died that week and we had to dig him a grave with the others inside the rickety fence on the hillside, and make him a coffin out of old boards in the leaky shop where tools were scarce.

The fact was that Tom and I were the fellow slaves who did the dirty work of this establishment. We carried out the slops. Other times we caulked a boat and whitewashed the hospital with slaked lime that the next rain washed off. We got the water system going from the pond up on the hill and only flooded the kitchen once. We patched the roof and set up stovepipes and put in glass and unloaded countless barrels of flour and food and tons of freight at the wharf. We were hospital orderlies when the doctor was operating before the nurses came; and every rainy day somebody got out the glass and spied the wireless man's old trousers a-flap on the distant Marconi station pole and one of us had a mile to row and four miles of swamp to run through after a message.

Well, after a bad week along came one of those sun-and-silver days and all the schooners had their sails hoisted drying. Tom and I just said "yes" to the doctor and the intern and both nurses and the housekeeper and the cook. We put our hands in our pockets and went up on the Indian Head. We sat there drinking blue enchantment right fresh off the horizon, forgetful that anyone ever

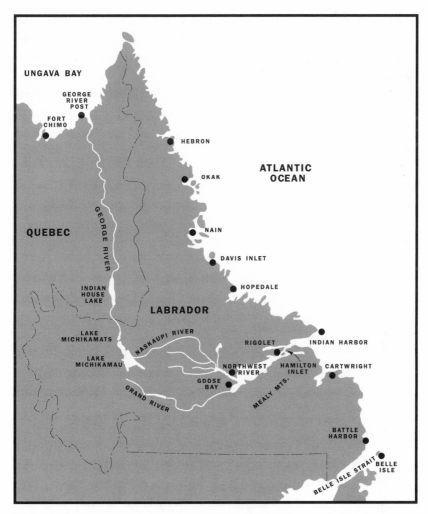

Map 2 Labrador as it looked during the time of these stories. In the 1960s and 1970s, the Smallwood and Ossokmanuan reservoirs, part of the huge Churchill Falls hydroelectric project, flooded a large portion of southwestern Labrador, completely erasing lakes Michikamau and Michikamats and radically changing the landscape of the region.

died since the world was born. And when we felt so free and wide we couldn't sit still any longer, we ran down the green south slope through the flaming fireweed and daisies and wild peas and bakeapple blossoms, over the black, striped ledges to the beach of white shell. We stripped and dove into the sea's clear liquid ice. It was so cold it burned like fire.

We came out purified and brand-new, and lay on a warm rock to let the salt dry on us. Tom generally told me about his girl, but I stuffed seaweed in my ears. Then we climbed the slope of our tree-less island and had a last look from the top before going down to the civilized side where people worked.

Toward the end of the afternoon, with still no smudge of smoke in the north haze, the wind shifted and grew damp. The sky turned gray, the sea slate. A fog bank rose up out of the horizon and hung a few miles offshore. Our silver days were few and did not last long. Perhaps that is why we felt them so.

Tom came up over the edge of the rock, a leather jacket over his blue jersey to break the wind, denim trousers, rubber boots. He stood on the summit, one hand in his bosom and declaimed to encircling space: "Roll on, thou mighty Ocean, roll. Suppose I tell you to stop rolling? Ah, well may you ask what then.

"Supper," he said. "My watch for awhile."

I went down to supper in the square, high-ceilinged dining room where the floor creaked even when the doctor carved codfish. The jolly intern, the grizzled doctor, the housekeeper, and the least pretty of the nurses were there for the eternal codfish in one of its infernal disguises. The intern was telling about the malingerer:

"After a week of most careful observation and tests, we have been unable to find anything wrong with him. He eats first-rate and sleeps like a top. So today I poked him under the left knee-cap and I said, 'When I press here do you feel a shooting pain just above your heart?' And he screwed up his face and moaned, 'O Doctor, I finds it wonnerful, right handy against me heart.' And would you believe it, I wiggled his right big toe and said, 'Can you feel a sharp ache in the back of your neck when I move your toe thus?' And he said it made a pain in the back of his neck that was worse than he could stand. He fooled his skipper into sailing him all the way from Nain to Hopedale so he could get down here and enjoy himself all summer."

"Well," said his senior, "we can't encourage that sort of thing and I mean to speak to him privately. But I venture to say that a month in a Newfoundland fishing vessel would make a rest in bed and plenty of good food a pleasant prospect for most any of us. We'll send him south by the steamer. He lives in Bonavista Bay, I believe?

"And that reminds me, Bud," he said, turning to me. "We are sending that bad rheumatism case, Captain Willett, home by this steamer. He is absolutely helpless, his heart is in bad shape and he is in pain, so go easy with the stretcher. And will you make yourself responsible for Captain Willett's bag of clothes if the steamer comes tonight? See that it is placed in the bunk with him, as I understand there is some money in it."

The rain was beating against the window and the fire roared in the wind-sucked stovepipe while we ate our dessert of cheese and crackers. The back door slammed and we heard Joe, the hospital's young Eskimo helper, stamp the wet off his boots and giggle as he said to the cook, "Steamer's comin'—sometime."

The least pretty nurse went off to relieve the most pretty nurse. The medicos went to the ward. The mail was bagged and everything made ready for the zero hour.

At nine-thirty I stumbled through the rain to the doctor's shack where my bed was. It was a portable cottage guyed with steel cables to ringbolts leaded into the rock ledge. In the tearing wind it was trembling like a Japanese paper house. Doctor came in soon, and together we put up the wooden two-by-four props from wall to wall, an invention of his own designed to prevent the wind from crushing the building flat. I got into bed, leaving my trousers tucked in my boots close beside the chair with sweater and oilskins and mitts. Doctor set the kerosene lamp on a chair beside his bed and commenced to read "The Ring and the Book." He always had to read himself to sleep, though one would have thought he would be tired enough to sleep standing up.

After an unusual gust, he laid the book on his knees and remarked, "By Jupiter, I've never in my life seen a place like this for wind. I wish you could have been here one night three summers ago. The harbor was boiling with solid foam picked right up off the water. Five schooners went ashore. Burdett had the *Kyle* hove to behind Pigeon Island. She had two anchors down and she steamed all night half-speed to keep them from dragging. No one could think of getting out to the steamer in the morning.

"Burdett was scared stiff, an odd chap, a timid soul, but not a bad skipper. If he were still master of *Kyle* we could depend on it he'd be snugged away in some harbor tonight. No fear of his showing up. But this fellow Clark! By George, the way he drives that ship is a miracle. Anyone else would pile her up twenty times a trip, running all night the way he does, fair or foul, in and out the narrow tickles, among the islands, fog, rain, ice, never a buoy or a light, making his stops as regularly as a suburban tram. There isn't a man on earth who knows this coast the way he does. Mark my words, he'll be along tonight about three o'clock when it's blackest. But you must get some sleep. It's your watch from twelve to two and Joe will call you." He went on with his book and I fell asleep.

Joe stood in the middle of the room, in his hand a lantern throwing shadows. Shining rain ran down his oilskins onto the floor and his round cheeks glistened. "Steamer's comin'," he chirped, and ran out the door. I looked at the clock. Ten of twelve.

Doctor was dressed before I was. He was buttoning his sou'wester under his chin when we heard her blow outside the harbor, "Whaw-w-w! Whaw-w-w-w!" Deep bass, ominous, making the already riven air tremble. A long monster afloat out there in the blackness, its scaly length lifted and rippled by the running combers, its yawning mouth agape, bellowing hoarsely for a victim.

We groped in the rain. Lights were springing up in the hospital. The prettiest nurse was in the ward fixing the stretcher for Captain Willett. Tom came in. I tied the Captain's clothesbag around my waist under the oilskins. He also had a suitcase, but that was already down at the wharf with the mail sack. Tom and I rolled him onto the stretcher and it hurt him badly.

The malingerer was there and dressed. I wondered if he knew we knew. The other patients were all awake, looking on with sleepy eyes. We covered the stretcher with a canvas, got him through the door and went down the long, slippery boardwalk. We walked as gently as we could, but he, poor fellow, gave a groan about every other step. The motorboat was at the wharf and Joe and the intern helped us lay the stretcher crosswise on the gunnels. He seemed to feel better with the boat rocking under him. Tom lifted a corner of the canvas. "How's that, Captain?"

"All shipshape, son," the sick man smiled.

Doctor came a-running, and with him at the tiller we shoved off. The intern and I stood on the foredeck hanging to the mast. Joe was at the engine, for he loved engines with a child's love of a marvelous toy. "Hang onto that stretcher," Doctor called cheerily. "We don't want to lose you, Captain."

"Twouldn't matter much," the Captain mumbled.

The shore dropped out as though it had fallen over the edge of an abyss. The rain stung and it was cold as winter. The booming surf on the point was all we had to guide us. Though the harbor was narrow, we might have been in mid-ocean for all we could see. The boat began to thrash and plunge as we got out onto the broader water. Now in the darkness round about we could hear the irregular, intermingled pung-pung-pungpung-pung of fishermen's exhausts, coming from all the coves and bights and tickles within a mile or two to see the floating palace, the herald of the other world, the news-bearer, the steamer.

We could make her out now, a low, slim ship, something like a destroyer, outlined in lights, pawing there impatient. Shouts came out of the dark, the hiss of steam, the throbbing of her pumps. Fishermen's boats were clustered three deep alongside and astern, squeaking and crunching when they touched, a man in each with a boathook or a sculling oar, fending off; fishermen watching their chance to jump from one to the other as they rose and fell, fisher-men swarming up the steamer's side and throwing a leg over the rail like attackers storming a citadel.

We rounded the stern and came up to the companion ladder slung on the port side. "Shut 'er off," Doctor called. We drifted in and our coiled painter sailed over the rail and hit the deck with a satisfying thwack. A sailor ran forward with it and brought us alongside the companionway, which was banging viciously. "Watch your feet," the sailor shouted. The boat rose half way up the wooden stair, then sank six feet below the bottom step.

Clark's huge head and shoulders loomed over the bridge wing above. "Go for'r'd and we'll hoist your man with the tackle!" he yelled.

The sailor on deck hauled us forward, passing our painter out-side each stanchion as he went. When we were abreast of the hatch, the cargo boom swung over, the winch rattled and the hook descended, a chain barrel-sling dangling from it. With four dou-bles of codline we lashed each corner of the stretcher to the barrel-sling. The bo's'n stood above holding the winch cable out from the ship's side. "Come up easy," he sang, and Captain Willett was whisked to the deck as smooth as glass.

Tom and I scrambled aboard on a line and carried him aft to the sickbay, which was also the steerage cabin. We fixed him comfort-ably in a bunk, and when it was over he sighed with relief. "You're a pair o' manhandlers all right," he grinned. "You lay another finger on me and I'll pitch you overboard, the two of ye." He had grit, and no mistake.

"Good luck, Captain," Tom said hurriedly.

"All right, b'y," he replied wearily.

The ship's doctor came in, an ancient pharmacist, and we told him Doctor would be there with instructions presently.

We hurried along the wet deck to the mailroom just forward, swung open the heavy oak door and stepped in. The mailman was a sandy-haired, ageless person with a cracked voice and every grain of gossip from eight hundred miles of coast on his tongue's tip. In one corner was his bunk, in the other a rack of open-mouthed mail sacks. Along the forward side of the cabin stood a long sorting table and opposite it a solid wall of pigeon holes, each bearing the name of one of the scores of little harbors and coves the steamer called at: Belle Isle, Battle Harbour, Cape Charles, Seal Islands, Fishing Ships, Hawke's Harbour, Occasional Harbour, Domino, Spotted Islands, Boulter's Rock, Gready, Cartwright, Rigolet, White Bear, Cut-throat, Ragged Islands, Emily, Holton, Makkovik and dozens more.

"Well, boys," he squeaked, "what's the news? I hear Jimmie Barnes' boy . . ."

"Yes," interrupted Tom, "he's in the hospital with an infected foot, but he's getting better. Got any mail for us?"

"Well, boys, all your mail's gone ashore in the boat to King's. But now here's something you won't see every day." With enormous enjoyment he handed Tom a letter postmarked Boston and addressed:

Mr. Thomas Witherspoon

Labrador

"Why don't you tell your friends, your street and number, hey? Oh, ho, ho!"

Tom was duly flabbergasted and we left swearing eternal friendship. On the way by, we stopped to smell the heat and oil and look down through the slippery steel engine room companionway at the gleaming arms below and the polished massive metal in curious shapes. Next a glance into the little stokehole hell to see them open the doors and the red glare light the heaver's naked shoulders. One of them had a pinched-out cigarette behind his ear. He slammed the furnace door with his shovel and reached for the butt.

All of it was new to us, every trip. To see electric lights, steam condensers, engines, fittings of this floating, man-built stronghold was like polishing Aladdin's lamp. We had grown used to such things as wood and rock and a lopsided grindstone ashore.

Cascades of water were falling from the boat deck up above. Around the forward hatch searchlights shone warm and yellow. The winch chattered and stopped and chattered again. Barrels and boxes in slings came up through the hatch and disappeared over the side. The mate stood at the winch levers, and now and again he tightened or loosened a small wheel above the drum. The piston flew in and out and the drum unrolled and rolled itself in cable. The mate watched with cat's eyes, and the two levers in his hands guided the swinging loads with relentless precision, no matter that the ship was rolling. Jimmie, the bos'n, leaned over the side and signaled with his hand. It was easy to drop a puncheon through the bottom of a dancing trap boat, and it had often been done.

The crew had news of every schooner up along or down along, and while they worked they dished it out in snatches to the fishermen. Everyone was drenched, everyone was shivering, everyone was awake. If the crew of this ship ever slept, no one knew when.

Inside the first-class quarters beneath the bridge, the passengers had to be asleep, missing all this, for the white-paneled stateroom doors were tight closed. Below, in the brightly lit corridor, a heavy brass port had been unbolted and swung open for a few minutes in harbor. Tom and I went down the carpeted, branching stairs, feeling the smooth mahogany bannisters with pagan joy. Ostensibly it was to talk with Sam, the steward, in the spick-and-span dining salon and get him to sell us a couple of oranges. But really it was to contrast the white, speckless woodwork and the shining brass, this strong interior elegance, with the black, ruthless night outside. It satisfied a craving, as a spoonful of rich syrup might. Never unthreatened, buried under seas, wallowing over—how did they keep this inner jewel unmarked by the elements?

We had to run up the narrow companionway for a hello to Captain Clark on the bridge. In cowhide seaboots and a thick gray ulster bulged by his barrel chest, he stalked the bridge, pausing now and again to pull aside the canvas wind screen and glare at the foredeck, his cap pulled down over his red eyes. He was a walrus of a man, with a voice like the bass notes of a viol.

"Ha!" he growled, looking us over. "Your own mothers wouldn't know ye, ye two bloomin' Huskimaws. Got ye out of bed, eh? Do ye good. A dirty night, sure enough. A good trip? Yes, good enough. All right, two weeks next Thursday, God willing."

Down on the deck there was hurry. She couldn't stay much longer. The last gasoline drums were going over the side. The winch chattered furiously. From up above Captain Clark bellowed down into the searchlit hatch, "Hey! Get done!"

"Whaw-w-w!" A jet of steam jumped from the funnel and the hideous blare smote the night again. On the fo'c'sle head the anchor winch started to thump. Chain rattled in the hawsehole. Fishermen scrambled for their boats, the ship already underway.

Bells clanged in the engine room, half astern, wheel hard over, full ahead. The sea thundered under her counter. Lines were flying, men were leaping. Fishermen's boats began to pung. Last words shouted.

She steamed away into the inky night, masthead lights lurching, bound for another reef-guarded harbor of rock, as though she were steered by smell.

ISLE OF DEMONS

**R**UTH KNEW she would live on an island when she married Fred Osborne. His father and grandfather had been lighthouse keepers along the St. Lawrence shores of the Canadian Labrador, men capable as seals in the endless struggle with the sea. She had scarcely married him before the newlyweds were assigned to Belle Isle, outermost beacon that guides trans-Atlantic ships groping through fog and ice for the estuary that leads to Quebec and Montreal.

They had a long, rough trip aboard the Canadian lighthouse tender *Aranmore*, stopping to supply other lighthouses on the way, and Ruth was seasick. When they arrived off the dark cliffs of Belle Isle, quite a sea was running. The captain called for a volunteer crew to man the surfboat. For the first time—but by no means the last—Ruth stood in an opening in the side of the ship where a great iron cattle-door had been thrown open, and watched the surfboat rise and fall below her. She aimed for a potato bag, and as the boat rose to the crest and the sailors who had her by each arm shouted "Jump!" she made her dizzy leap. Everywhere the surf was booming.

As they came round the shoulder of a rocky island and into the treacherous anchorage known as Black Joke, she looked up and saw a solid wall of water roaring down on them, and above it on a cliff a white cross glistening. The cross commemorated the drowning of two fisher boys in Black Joke—two of many.

The boat's crew left them at the stone dock with a barrel of flour, a barrel of sugar, a bag of potatoes and a trunk. Four workmen had come ashore with them to repair the lighthouse, and the Osbornes were to board them, but Ruth didn't know it at the time. They climbed to the house by the ninety steps cut into the rock, and the vessel steamed away.

Ruth built a fire in the range but it was rusted out and a huge flame filled the oven. None of their furniture had come ashore. They had no table, no chair, no bedstead. The trunk she had thought filled with blankets and dishes and silver was the wrong one, containing useless trinkets. Some of the Newfoundland schoonermen who fish about the island during July and August took in the workers, but she had to get meals for three days for six people out of a barrel of sugar, a barrel of flour, and a sack of potatoes. Fred and Ruth slept between two mattresses, there being no blankets.

On the old charts Belle Isle is called Isle of Demons. An eerie heap of rock and cliff and moss, it stands alone in the stormy Straits, eighteen miles from the southern tip of Labrador, thirty miles from the northern cape of Newfoundland. There are no trees, and even the single-budded pussy willows push their stems horizontally in the moss to escape the bitter winds. It would be easy to imagine that prehistoric monsters still live among the black-water ponds of the island's crest, and as a matter of fact, polar bears do sometimes roam there in the spring.

Fog shrouds the island half the time in summer, and on one occasion the fog alarm was sending its deep blare out to sea for 132 hours without a stop. Fred and his helper had little rest at such times, because one of them must always be on watch, and it was an iron-bound rule that the two compressor engines must be alternated at regular intervals and the idle one taken down, inspected and greased. Nothing must go wrong with the light or the fog alarm—ever.

The fog came in wisps and tatters, it came in banks and shoals, it came creeping in the quiet and pouncing in the winds. And often there were strange clear lanes to leeward of the icebergs that drifted south from Greenland all summer. The fog plays strange tricks on the Isle of Demons, with sharply dividing lines that leave a schooner's mains'l hidden in the cold mist while her fores'l and bowsprit stand out sharp in the sunshine. Many a time Ruth saw half their house in fog and half in the clear, and even an apparition of half a man floating over the rocks. That would be skipper Fred coming up to supper from the light, a reassuring reality standing six feet two, weighing 200, and giving her a hug.

Just off the light were Mad Rocks, where combers boiled over a reef. Nearby was Wreck Cove. The charts called the Osborne's place Misery Point. But that was before they got there.

Newfoundlanders who braved this place for a few weeks a year soon found out Ruth was a trained nurse. A bearded schoonerman came to the house and said, "I got pups, Ma'm."

"Pups?"

"Yes, Ma'm, and I feel so bad since I had the last batch I can't fish."

"You mean *you* had pups?"

"Yes, Ma'm. Last Monday I had three, and Wednesday I had five, and come Friday I had seventeen."

He rolled up his sleeve and showed her a crop of salt water boils which, she discovered, go by the name of water pups. He was very sick and his back was covered with them. There was no one to take care of him, so the Osbornes had him in bed for three weeks, hardly able to move. Fishermen constantly soaked by the cold salt spray are prone to these infections, as well as to septic fingers and hands.

At first she needed an interpreter for the strange Newfoundland fisher talk. A man groaned, "Me kinkorn's wunnerful and I can't glutch." This might have meant most anything; however, she found that *kinkorn* meant throat and *glutch* was obsolete English for swallow.

Wonderful is confusing because it can mean either *very good* or *very bad*. She once said to a fisherman, "How is your cook today?"

"Wunnerful!"

It turned out that the seventeen-year-old girl who was cook aboard his schooner was nearer dead than alive. "But Skipper Fred's 'oman—wunnerful smart she be—brung 'n 'roun'."

In late August the fishermen sailed away to the south. The *Aranmore* came twice a year with mail and supplies for the Osbornes in August and November. Pack ice ground against the island all winter, churned into chaos by three currents: the Labrador current driving south, the St. Lawrence sweeping into the sea, and tides that run eight and ten knots past the points. Sunny days in winter the ice was sometimes locked silent, and you'd be tempted to think dog teams could cross it by a quick dash to the blue Labrador shore. But it was almost certain death to try, for it might start grinding and rafting again at any moment, roaring against the rocks with such force you'd expect it to pulverize the island in one night. Because of the pack ice they were more isolated than they would have been in Baffin Island, where the ice makes solid dog team roads in all directions. On their island no one could leave or arrive, come hell or high water, life or death, between Christmas and the following June.

November of that first year Ruth had to leave on the *Aranmore* because she was going to have a baby. The child was born in the States in February, and her father never saw her until August when Ruth got back again on the next supply ship to the good old Isle of Demons. They had a new range, crates of hens, a fine supply of vegetables, and new curtains.

They had a telephone that was supposed to connect their station on the ocean end of Belle Isle with another lighthouse twelve miles away on the inner point of the island where a government radio station was located. But the island being solid rock, it had been impossible to set telephone poles, so the lines had been laid on the bare rock. Fred ground the crank and shouted into the mouthpiece like a mate bawling orders in a gale, and it was about three times a summer that he got a faint, whispered, "Hello," in return, and not much else.

As well as being a trained nurse, Ruth had once studied elementary teaching. By the time she had two daughters, the older one needed schooling, and it wasn't long before both girls were studying in "The Belle Isle Institute of Learning and Seminary for the Enlightenment of Progressive Females," taught by a person who was known around the house as "Dearie," though the girls changed her name annually in the schoolroom; for who ever heard of having the same teacher year after year? In successive years Ruth was known as Miss Simpson, Miss Black, Miss White, Miss Jimpsie, and one year Miss Black-and-Blue.

Fred made the children sand tables. They began with crayoning and numbers and letters and clay modeling, working up from there. Ruth sent for *Ellson Readers* and a *Book of Knowledge,* as well as all sorts of reading, writing, and 'rithmetic books, and the school gradually became quite professional, with regular Christmas and Easter vacations, a blackboard, graduation ceremonies, a globe, home-made songs, dances, poetry, and home-made paintings on the wall. Before the girls were five, they could read quite well.

The coming of the supply steamer with letters and surprises brought on such scurrying and commotion as can hardly be imagined. She'd be coming over the horizon, and the Osborne family would be studying her with the telescope, when the barometer began to fall and the breeze piped up. She'd turn around and steam away, getting smaller and smaller till she disappeared. Everybody's face looked kind of white and strained. But after a few days of unloading supplies at some more sheltered light along the Gulf shore, she'd reappear and make another try.

All the tons of supplies came ashore in a surfboat towed by a shoal-draft motor launch. Several times while the *Aranmore* lay at anchor unloading, the fierce tides caught her and she began to drag. The ship had to wind in her chain and jog to and fro under power while the unloading continued. One hundred barrels of oil it took to supply the light and the fog alarm engines. The August boat usually brought those, along with the scores of blessed letters from families and friends. There was no time to answer letters in all the commotion of unloading freight; the answers had to wait until November. And in November the answers had to wait until the following August. Most years the lighthouse keeper received a live ox, unloaded by a sling harness into the surfboat and brought ashore to be kept until freeze-up, when they butchered it for the winter's beef. The boat's crew tied the bullock's head down tight to a thwart in the surfboat and hoped he wouldn't kick the bottom out. But one year the bullock got his head loose coming in and began to thrash around. A tough bos'n from the *Aranmore* became panicky and jumped overboard. He was so mad to find himself in the icy water that he climbed aboard the surfboat again and whacked the bullock with an oar until *it* jumped overboard. They got a rope around the bullock's neck and it had to swim nearly half a mile to shore.

Most years the Osbornes ordered hens so they could have eggs during the winter. Once in the commotion of freight day, Ruth went down the cliff road to the dock and found that their team of husky-dogs had got loose and eaten the heads off every single one of the crated hens. Three dozen hens lay in the crates, not one of whom would ever stick her head out for a look-around again. It was necessary to get busy and can chicken meat.

Fred had an old Ford truck for carrying the tons of oil and coal and potatoes up from the landing to the lighthouse. The road was a zigzag, precariously narrow, blasted out of the rock wall. It had two turns so sharp and narrow that you had to stop and back up toward the abyss in order to get around them. There was nowhere to run the truck except on the cliff road hauling up supplies, and this he did for eight years. By that time it had no fenders, no light, no doors, no upholstery, no horn. The battery was tied onto the side with a piece of wire, and he wound rope around the tires in place of chains. He was bringing up sacks of potatoes one slippery day when the brakes altogether failed to hold her at the second hairpin turn. Ruth was watching as the old wreck slipped backward toward the cliff. The hired men jumped out when the back wheels were almost at the edge. Fred twisted the wheel hard over and hopped out as one of the rear tires began to spin in midair and three potato bags slid over the cliff. They were all holding their breath expecting the truck to crash on the rocks below, when the front wheels locked, caught in a rock and held her there, half over. Ruth was sorry, for she knew that meant Fred would hitch up a block and tackle and resurrect the old car.

Next time a lighthouse inspector came ashore to stay a week on his yearly visit, Fred rode him up the cliff road. The inspector stepped out at the top white as a sheet, hardly knowing whether to be furious or thankful, too shaken to be either. "I wouldn't ride in that thing again," he said, "if my job depended on it."

That night Ruth got him aside and said to him, "Fred has to ride in that thing, you know. There is no other way to get up the freight. Don't you think something should be done about it?"

The following year what did the Osbornes see, crosswise on the surfboat, making her roll dangerously as she made in through Black Joke tickle, but a brand-new pearl gray Chevrolet delivery truck, with headlights, red leather upholstery, cigarette lighter, ashtray, heater in the cab, and two horns and a mirror! They all got in and toured back and forth on the smooth rocks between the light and the house, looking in the mirror at the sea and blowing both horns at once.

The delays in receiving things sent away for were hardly credible. In August Ruth sent to a department store in the States for a particular dress of cornflower blue that she had seen advertised. In November came a letter saying, "Our stock of this model in cornflower blue is exhausted. Shall we send navy? Kindly advise, and be assured it is our highest happiness to serve you, etc."

"The fools," said she. By the following August boat she mailed a letter directing them to send the navy one by all means. In November, a year having now elapsed, came a letter from the store, "We no longer stock this model in any color. May we send you something else. We enclose our catalogue. Kindly advise, and be assured it is our highest happiness, etc." She got a piece of homespun from the wife of a mainland fisherman who raised sheep, and made a better dress than they could ever have sent anyway. "Sour grapes," said Fred. But it was really very pretty.

In the winter, evening after evening with the earphones on Fred taught himself the Morse code by listening to the ships at sea. He studied radio in all its phases, got his license, and by studying and experimenting on his own, and consulting with experts at the west end where they had a big radio direction finding station, he built his own sending set. It was one of the grandest things that ever happened. They would hear that snow was falling by the Great Whale River, tulips were out in Amsterdam, and Aunt Em had a cold.

In the summertime, Fred sent hundreds of necessary messages for the fishing crews, ordering salt and supplies, so after a while the government equipped him with a more powerful transmission and receiving set. One wild December night Ruth and Fred were sitting in their cozy living room close by the warm stove, Fred with earphones on listening to the short-wave stations and the ships, when he suddenly held up his hand and said, "Sh-h! An s.o.s." It was a coaster sinking in the storm not a hundred miles from Belle Isle, sending her last message: "The officers and crew send their undying love to their dear ones at home, and may God bless and keep them every one. Good-bye."

That was the winter when a January storm blew two of the dining room windows in. It was evening and they were playing cards in the adjacent living room. The cards left the table and hit the wall with a spat. A newly baked cake was showered with flying glass and had to be thrown away. It took all a man's strength to hold up a board while the openings were nailed shut.

Ruth found that if she was to run the Female Seminary effi-
ciently she had to have a maid to help with washing and cleaning
and cooking. Some of the young women stayed two or three years
and were very fine indeed. They came from tiny settlements on the
Labrador shore, and in those days Labrador people, under juris-
diction of the Colony of Newfoundland, paid an import duty rang-
ing as high as 65 percent on linens and clothing. But by living at a
Canadian lighthouse station the young woman could order her
trousseau duty-free from Canada. After a year or two of being the
belle of Belle Isle, she took home an outfit that made her a highly
desirable miss, though she probably was anyway. The young
women always called Ruth "Dearie," and after a while it didn't
sound so funny.

So many of the summer fishermen came to them for help that
the first thing they knew, they found themselves running a four-
bed, unofficial nursing station, completely at their own expense.
They tried to get financial aid, but the patients were Newfoundland fishermen, the island was Canadian territory, and the two
governments weren't cooperating very closely at the time. In one
summer Ruth gave over four hundred treatments for various ail-
ments and tore up seven aprons, one sheet, six old pillow slips, two
of Fred's shirts and a housedress to use as bandages and dressings.

Ruth missed trees. Always when she went "outside" and saw
trees again, big green trees against the sky, tears would start from
her eyes. And she missed playmates for her girls, too. She could
teach them all right; she taught them both to play the little organ
they had, and as for school work, she gave them regulation department of education examinations that the superintendent in Prince
Edward Island furnished. These they passed with flying colors. But
they needed the give-and-take of competition—or so she thought.
Once when they were out for a sojourn in the green farming country of Prince Edward Island, the two girls went out alone for a walk.
The older one gripped the little one's hand, and they moved with
caution, for on Belle Isle they had a two-hundred-foot cliff not a
rod from the house, and in winter they dared not go near it for fear
of the wind's blowing them over the icy edge. Ruth saw them inch-
ing down the road, but by and by they came back shouting,
"Mother, Mother, we went the longest way and it's all flat and we
never came to a single cliff!"

It was things like that that got them going on The New House, a dream for which they saved and planned. It would be in Canada in a place where the seasons were balmier and the trees grew tall. For years they drew plans and pictures, and Ruth made curtains for the hypothetical living room, and the maid hooked rugs with schooners and lighthouse pictures worked in. In fact, the rugs were drawn in on the floor plan and crayoned by the girls. "This is your playhouse, isn't it, Dearie," said Betty Jean.

Winter storms were kind of cozy. The house was very solidly built, had an eight-foot cellar blasted out of the rock, and was anchored with iron bolts. But most every summer storm brought some kind of trouble that the Osbornes were involved in. Twelve schooners have been known to go down in Black Joke in one storm. It looked like a good little anchorage but that was the cruel part of the Joke. When gales were blowing, a mysterious and irresistible undertow surged through the tickle with such force that no boat could live. Many's the time the family saw schooners' sails flutter up and watched them fly before a gale out across the purple straits. Once, three schooners got sucked under in a storm there. They had anchors out astern and were moored bow-on to ring-bolts in the rock by steel cables and chains. You could hear the cables pop like strings. The crew tried to hold the last of them by two-inch chains fastened to her bulwarks on the port side. A surge of current came through and tore the side off the vessel, leaving a few timbers thrashing about at the ends of the chains, and that was all. The men got ashore on the rocks, but there was not a spar or a single splinter of wreckage ever found around the shores of Black Joke. The undertow carried everything far out to sea.

Summer wasn't the best time by any means. As far as food went, it was starvation time, with the frozen beef all gone, berries not yet ripe, vegetables spoiling. It was the steady stream of ships passing the island that was exasperating. The great ships bound for England, the other ships outward bound for Australia and round the world or rolling home, cruise ships for Bermuda, freighters, yachts, and coasters—Ruth stood on the cliff and watched them pass, so near and yet so far. At night the liners slid by like jewels.

Strange as it may seem, when the snows came and the ice, and when navigation closed, the family settled in with a feeling of real happiness. Everybody was gone and the Osbornes were on their own. The cellar was stocked with food by the ton. The two five-thousand-gallon fresh water cisterns under the house had been carefully filled, and the pipe from the pond above as carefully drained.

They celebrated all holidays, both American and Canadian, and never let anybody's birthday go by without festivities. Ruth was all the summer hiding away odd, peculiar presents for special occasions like April Fool's Day and Father's Day and Valentine's Day.

One Christmas the girls decorated the whole house with red and green, and in the living room were red and white bells covered with silver stars which Betty Jean and Ruth had cut out. Over the ceiling was stretched a tinsel spider web that glittered at night. There was wrapping paper all over everywhere, and whisperings of secrets between Daddy and Sally and Daddy and Betty and Daddy and Dearie. A light man and a radio operator from the west came crunching in over the snow to visit for the holidays, and Christmas Eve the school put on its inevitable concert which consisted of songs by all, recitations by the Misses Osborne, and a speech by the principal (Fred). It was very well attended by an appreciative audience. Daddy was proud, Dearie was pleased, and Miss White just glowed. There was a play too. Everybody wanted to be an actor and the difficulty was to have anybody left over for the audience.

Each of the twenty-five dolls and animals that belonged to the girls had hung up its stocking. Some got caps, some pins, some new collars, and the oldest dolls each had a raisin, a piece of popcorn and a peanut. The children went off to bed too tired to dream of tomorrow's doings, while Fred and Ruth decorated the Christmas tree and opened up their own presents, one of which was a check to buy something for the new house.

Christmas morning was a scramble among packages from aunts, uncles, cousins, grandparents. Fred had made a new table for one of the girls, with a drawer in it, and two dolls' beds for the other.

Mom cooked the dinner, a tremendous affair of roast beef, cream potatoes, carrots and peas, fruit cup, pineapple salad, jellies, pickles, ice cream with chocolate sauce, nuts, pumpkin pie. The radio was dead so they didn't get a particle of Christmas music, but they all played cribbage at night, and at eleven had a little snack just to keep in trim.

After New Year's there were a lot of fox tracks around so Fred put out a great many traps. Everybody had hobbies, especially Fred, and he was able to follow them earnestly now that the Straits were frozen and the light was shut down. He was making furniture and replacements for the gear around the station. When he came there, the fog alarm engines were so old they were condemned. But he was a machine tool expert and could make not only parts, but tools for making the parts. He renewed the engines till they were practically perfect. He dabbled in hammered copper and could work in steel, iron, or brass. He once made a brass doorknob and a brass replica of the lighthouse. He had been through several correspondence school courses, one in electricity, another in radio, and now he was doing a couple on drafting and mechanical drawing. It was a handicap that he couldn't send in his papers to be corrected at intervals, but he just did them all at once and sent in the lot. He was also much interested in aviation and thought he ought to have a little plane for landing on the Belle Isle ponds with pontoons in summer and skis in winter.

The children had special projects. For instance, they took some species of fish, drew pictures of it, also detail sections of gills, fin, eye; looked it up in the *Book of Knowledge* and another encyclopedia; learned all they could about its food, habits, migrations; and then wrote a composition about it, and a poem. The composition was a letter to some mythical little boy who lived in the middle of a desert and had never seen a fish. In the course of all this they had practice in art, composition, grammar, spelling, reading, and writing.

Winter evenings Ruth was always busy preparing a sort of hope chest for the New House, sewing linens, towels, bedspreads, bureau scarves. She had a horrid way of hiding Fred's gift shirts and socks and telling him he couldn't have them until his old ones were in ribbons, and (CHORUS) "They're to use in the New House." He said it was getting so she went around saving his cigarette butts for the New House.

Before they knew it, spring was upon them in a rush, the sun was bright, there were blue leads in the ice, the birds were coming back, the wild geese were bound north, the girls were taking their sand tray out of doors to make a cold frame out of it. Their father put a heavy piece of half-inch lighthouse glass over it and hoped it wouldn't blow away. In a hollow of rock they planted a little garden of lettuce, radishes, carrots, and potatoes. The best year they had five meals of turnip greens, harvested a quart dipperful of miniature potatoes, and the radishes grew as big as marbles.

The girls began to ramble around, picking early wildflowers like the arctic rose that blooms right up through snowdrifts, and getting reacquainted with their favorite nooks among the rocks: Flower Road, Wild Iris Way, Fragrant Valley, Smiling Pool. They had their imaginary playmates too, fifty paper dolls, all with names, who lived in a playhouse that Fred had built. All the paper dolls were poor orphans, and the orphanage was run by two very wealthy women called the Strange Lady Sisters. Sometimes the Strange Ladies sewed clothes and picked berries to make jam for the orphans of Strange Lady Home. Every spring the paper orphans staged a concert in a miniature theater with countless props.

Whenever Ruth tells people about her years on Belle Isle, they usually suppose she is a great sailor and just loves the sea. "But I know too much about the sea to just love it. I've known too many women who, with husband and eldest son lost at sea, have had to dry their eyes and send a second son out beyond the harbor heads." A northern Newfoundland family in those days could either fish or starve.

"The fact is that I dislike the sea intensely. How did I live there then so happily? It is hard to explain, but I will try. You must know that every window of our house looked out upon the ocean or the gray rocks; there was no getting away from them. One day I was feeling unusually sad about the unending sternness of it all, so sad that even the little willow bush outside the house did not comfort me, for all its fortitude. That was the only plant that stood up straight, two gnarly feet into the air, while all other growing things crawled on the rocks. I just happened to wander into the dining room and there on the floor I picked up a torn page from a magazine and read a poem. This is what it said:

> Oh, weary am I of this gaunt gray land
> And the ceaseless ebb and flow
> Of the hungry sea as it surges in
> To crash on the rocks below;

> Of the blinding fogs and the cutting winds,
> And the bleached contorted tree
> Gripping the soil with its knotted roots,
> In its stubborn will to be.

For I was bred in a kinder land,
And felt myself as one
With the rich black earth and the slanting rain
And the fierce compelling sun.

But my man is here, and the sea he loves
Is linked with his love for me;
So I bide me here with the rocks and tides
And the brave old twisted tree.

And there was my case stated for me, even to the rocks and the tree and the man."

They were there fourteen years, with a winter out every three or four years. When the time came for the Osbornes to leave Belle Isle, the fishermen had a brass plaque made in St. John's which said, "To Skipper Fred. A friend in need is a friend indeed." There was another one for Ruth which read, "To Mrs. Osborne. For kindness rendered in sickness and health." No other gift has ever touched them so.

And the Osbornes did get their New House—in the green and fertile country of Prince Edward Island, one of the finest areas of Canada. Fred became chief lighthouse inspector for all Gulf of St. Lawrence stations, traveling aboard a new and more powerful successor to the old *Aranmore*. The keepers of those lonely lights knew that no matter how bad the ice or fog or storm he'd land their supplies somehow. Ruth says in her straightforward fashion, "I'm proud to be his wife."

PASSING THE TIME

The principal character in this story is Australian Trained Nurse Kate Austen, in charge for the winter at North West River hospital. A year after the events related here, she became Mrs. Elliott Merrick.

IT WAS NOT EVEN DAYLIGHT when I heard the stovelid clang and spruce kindling begin to crackle. That was Sarah Jane. My room was so far below zero that when I jumped out of bed the pillow came with me, stuck to my hair by the frost from my breathing. Outside, along the tops of the Mealy Mountains the day was baring its teeth in a sanguine glare. The wind on the bay looked so cruel as it stirred the blue shadows with drift that it didn't seem possible we could stand the cold out there. But that's the way with lots of jobs early in the morning. I put on my woollens and my sealskin traveling pants, my socks and duffel slippers and leggings and moccasins, my sweaters too. I packed my clothes bag with spare socks and mittens in case we should get wet, and I took my sealskin boots on the chance of a thaw. You never know what will happen on a trip.

Down in the hall was a pile of gear: sleeping bag tied up with rope, the medicine chest, the grub box stuffed full. No matter how full the grub box was, it was always empty when we got back, for the houses where we stopped never failed to be short of something. Sarah Jane and Pearlie had baked some 'lasses bread which was particularly delicious on trips. While I ate my porridge, I could hear Jim squeaking up and down outside, harnessing the team.

"Some more coffee, Miss?" said Sarah Jane.

"Try some redberry jam?" said Pearlie.

The two wardsmaids were so good to me, it made me almost

embarrassed. Odd that we three with such different backgrounds should be closer than most sisters. I told them what to do for the patients in the ward, and left.

Outside, the air was fiendish. It made me almost ill with anguish to see Jim take off his mittens and barehanded bind all our gear to the sledge with those clever hitches he is so proud of. There was frost in our eyelashes, and in the dogs' eyelashes. We covered our noses and cheeks with our mittens as we felt them freezing.

We were off, down the bank with a lurch and a yell, the dogs glad to run and get warm. Then the bitter wind began to creep between our mittens and our cuffs, began to make our feet ache already. Once beyond the point and headed down the bay, Daisy, our leader, knew she should make for Green Island, blue and far away, she had been so often before.

Jim and I turned our backs and faced astern, pulling our fur hoods close about us while we watched the bay catch alight with silver diamonds and the sky melt from the pale robin's-egg to the deep, lovely turquoise of a perfect winter's day. We were oddly silent on trips. Sometimes we went for hours without saying anything.

As the sun rose higher, it tempered the frost, the sledge runners didn't squeak so much, and the team picked up speed. After Green Island had been left behind, our noses didn't hurt when we stuck them out into the breeze. Jim slowed the dogs so we could have a run on the crunching snow. I trotted behind, and it didn't matter about me, how slow I ran, or whether I fell. But Jim ran beside the forward end of the komatik where he could hop on at a moment's notice if the dogs began a spurt as they often do when they smell a seal hole. They will leave a fellow, like as not, if they get a chance, and Heaven knows where they'll go, wrecking the sledge and scattering the gear and ruining their harness on the way.

We hopped on again, tingling and excited, and all of a sudden a great joy flooded me. It had been impossible to start, it was so cold and grim and miserable. But here we were, miles from home already in the sunshine. Already the hills of home were blue behind us, the sun warm, the dogs galloping, the komatik surging. The daily miracle had engulfed us again and I was ashamed that only an hour ago existence had been a burden and oblivion in my bed the only joy.

Kneeling on the furs at the head of the sledge, Jim lit his pipe, which was always a sign of something, either good or bad.

The silver blue and wild sweetness of the bay on sunny winter mornings is more like paradise than earth. Twenty miles wide here, stretching ahead 190 miles to the sea, it was a great white highway of dreams. But I never knew anything that could flatten dreams quicker than a winter gale on Hamilton Inlet.

Hour after hour, sometimes five miles from land, we made a beeline down the bay from point to point. Just before noon we boiled the kettle on one of them. The dogs lay licking themselves. The kettle began to jump on its hanging stick, and Jim rubbed his hands before the blaze.

When the shadows of the land were creeping, and the cold was getting fierce again, we swung in. We were there, at Sabasquasho, a little river-mouth settlement of two houses, one deserted. The river and the shores were drifted deep in whiteness that was violet now.

The inside of Mrs. Edward Michelin's house was a mess. Nobody came to greet us. We just walked in. And there was Mrs. Michelin, her face a mass of sores, one shoulder and arm swollen and helpless, obviously hardly able to bear her pain, sitting up in bed telling Effie, aged seven, how to get tea for us. All that Effie was doing was to muddle with a heap of dirty dishes. It didn't take me a minute to discover that Mrs. Michelin had a bad case of septicemia.

Marjorie, a sweet little girl of eleven who might have been a great help to her mother, was sitting on the couch nursing a scalded leg. I had heard about that leg a month before, and had sent down dressings and directions. I'd supposed it was well by now, but no. From ankle to knee it was infected. Marjorie smiled sadly. She was rocking the squalling, starved-looking new baby that had laid Mrs. Michelin so low. The baby reminded me of a sparrow before its feathers come—all eyes and mouth, the latter wide open. "I ain't much good," said Marjorie, "and he's worse." There was also a small boy of eight, thin and dirty.

Jim had a look around, and went out to feed the dogs. Then we could hear him splitting wood.

Where to start. It was hard to know in this upside-down place. I wanted first of all to get the baby quiet, so I washed him and treated his sore buttocks and discharging umbilicus. He had been having watery condensed milk every hour, they said, but by the look of the bottle he had been sucking at it continuously for days. I made up a Klim milk formula and asked Marjorie to feed it to him while I fixed a basket to serve as his crib. (He had been sleeping with his mother.) Harold was seven days old and a living proof if ever I saw one of the durability of the newborn infant. Now that he was fed, I put him into the basket and threatened to deal drastically with any of the children who picked him up or rocked him. Having been fed and rocked ever since his birth, Harold found the new idea hard to accept, but we persisted, and soon he was asleep.

Blessed quiet! Now for Mrs. Michelin. In addition to her other sufferings, she had swollen and inflamed eyes. Her bed in the little room just off the kitchen faced an uncurtained window. The glare from the whiteness outside must have been awful on sunny days, and I had no doubt she was suffering from snowblindness. I bathed her eyes, covered them with a black handkerchief, turned the bed around and shaded the window with a dark coat ready for tomorrow. She had a high fever, no appetite, and what seemed like a bad case of septicemia. After sponging her and making her bed up fresh, I started in with the time-honored treatment of long hot douches, and felt a mental sag and a premature backache as I looked forward to a vista of these laborious treatments continued every four hours for Heaven knows how long.

"Where did you get this strained shoulder?" I asked her, for I couldn't figure that out. But she wasn't able to help me; she didn't know. Feeling a little more comfortable then, she took a little nourishment and I set her to drinking water, which she had been denying herself.

Next it was supper. They had nothing in the house except bread, tea, sugar and oatmeal. The children hadn't been able to get any rabbits or partridges, and the corn meal and bean supply had run out. I opened a few cans of vegetables from the grub box and made soup for everyone. Hungry as the children were, they ate with a certain diffidence. It was partly that they were shy and partly that cycles of starvation and plenty were no novelty to them. The molasses bread seemed to them too good to be true, but they could hardly be prevailed upon to take a second slice. Figgy cake, they called it, because it had raisins in it.

Then the dishes needed washing, and Marjorie's leg had to be dressed. A permanent part of my kit was a bundle of old sheets.

Some of these I cut up to make diapers for Harold, as he had no others. I gave Mrs. Michelin another irrigation treatment, tucked the children in, and crept into my sleeping bag on the floor at twelve o'clock, setting the alarm for four. Jim kept the fire going at intervals all night, which was a blessing, as the cold was intense enough to cover nailheads on the inner wall with deep frost and make the timbers give a loud crack every little while. I only heard the loudest ones. Harold, for the first time in his life, slept all night.

Next morning it was warmer, but snowing. Jim said he could find his way all right, so, since the team was needed at the hospital and I'd be here awhile, I told him to go back and come again in five days. I wasn't worried about him, because Jim could find his way through anything.

There's something cozy about a snowy day. It just shut us in and left us to ourselves to get things running smoothly here. While bathing her poor swollen face and cracked lips, I asked Mrs. Michelin, "Where do you suppose you picked up this infection anyway?"

She didn't seem to know and didn't care and couldn't talk much, but Marjorie, who was putting on some coffee from the good old komatik box, piped up, "Mrs. Huntley come from Mulligans to take care of Ma, 'count of Harold, 'n' she had a sore finger."

"She did, eh?"

"Yes, 'n' it got so bad she had to go home after a couple of days."

Probably that was it, I decided, and made a mental note to stop at Mulligans and see Mrs. Huntley, who had quite a reputation as a midwife. I wanted her to know, for future reference, what trouble she had caused here.

"Now, children," I said, "we're going to work hard at cleaning up the house, and then we'll have a party. We'll have some tomatoes and raisin cookies out of the komatik box, what do you say?"

The famous, fabulous komatik box! That met with a response. Wesley, the eight-year-old, filled the woodbox and set to splitting for a while until Effie should have time to saw with him on the two-handled crosscut. Marjorie's leg was a little better and she wanted to do something, so I gave her a pair of Wesley's pants to patch. She did a very good job on them, and at the same time kept her leg quiet. Wesley chopped open the water hole for us, and I carried up most of the water. They had a pretty good little kitchen range, old but still sound. The wood was green spruce and no great shakes to burn, but we could manage as long as we kept the firebox stuffed, and the oven filled with drying chunks.

I showed Marjorie how to bathe and change Harold, impressing her with the necessity for regular three-hourly feedings, as it seemed to me she would be a big factor in carrying on when I left. I spent a long time treating Mrs. Michelin, bathing her, changing the bed again, rubbing her back, greasing her lips, combing the tangles from her hair and oiling the knots that would not come out—all this over a period of time, letting her rest in between because she was so weak. She accepted a little broth I had had simmering, and then, as she seemed refreshed and comfortable, I closed the door, telling her to sleep while I took care of things.

Since it was now two o'clock, the children and I were starving. Early in the morning we had put on a fine big stew of canned meat and vegetables with rice and stale breadcrumbs and anything else we could find. How we did enjoy it, and then the raisin cookies and tomatoes. Tomatoes are called fruit here, the rarest of treats. It seemed we had accomplished wonders already. The children were glad to have a leader once more, and eager to get to work again because they were proud to do things for the nurse.

Wesley said he was pretty sure he knew a place where he could catch some trout, and he caught four good big ones which we fried for supper.

Mrs. Michelin had had such a good sleep, and more to eat. By evening she talked and seemed a lot better. I was encouraged by the drop in her temperature. The trout was good, the house was clean, floor newly scrubbed, Effie and Wesley had sawed "a monster heap, look and see, Miss," the woodbox was full, the water bucket on the bench was full too, and Harold slept quietly between feeds, accustomed to the cruel new regime already.

"We was skeered of you, a little, at first," said Wesley, coming and standing by my chair after supper.

"Nonsense, I wouldn't hurt a flea. Suppose I cut your hair now, and then you can all have a bath." They looked like different beings after this beautifying process, and I said, "Come on, I'll show you a game here on the table. You can play too, Effie. You take a lot of matches and make a square with four of them like this. Then another four on top, and you see how tall a tower you can make."

They thought it was wonderful. I was overhauling some of their buttons and rips while I talked to Marjorie. "Where is your father's hunting place?" I asked her.

"Oh, up Grand River somewheres."

"You don't know where, how far?"

"Somewheres near Horseshoe Rapids, he says."

"Do you know where that is?"

"No, Miss."

"We women ought to know about the country the way the men do," I said. "The bays and harbors and islands and shoals, and the rivers. It's lots of fun we miss, just doing dishes and mending socks. Have you ever been down the bay?"

"Oh yes, once. I been to North West River too."

"Let's draw a map, eh? You draw me a map of Sabasquasho River from here up as far as you know it. Here's a pencil and paper."

We had lots of fun. She showed me camping places and berry banks and fishing spots as much as six miles up the Sabasquasho. I drew for her the shore from here to North West River, with Long Point, Big Bight, Butter and Snow, Fred Rich's, Green Island. The maps were crude and sketchy, but they were the sort of thing one should know around here to make life interesting.

It was a pleasant evening, and they went happily off to their little wooden beds, clean and well fed for the first time since their mother had been laid up. I tucked them in, gave them each a hug, and then went back to the kitchen and sat by the stove awhile. It did seem strange, the only one awake in somebody's household, to think how many families I had entered into and been part of at various times. Many of the things you do you don't get paid for. Of course you don't do them for the pay. I decided you do them because they need doing and there's nobody else who can or will. For a time you are the mother, and then you go away and are the mother somewhere else. Sitting there alone I realized that I was beginning to get a little uncertain about the roaming life. To hurt oneself always with the wonder of the world—was that well, forever? What was I roaming for? If only I could get inside of life, not just see it and touch it, but be it. I had seen enough mothers to know that what I wanted most was children of my own. I was on the outside, looking in, on the outside traveling round the edges of experience. It did not matter that some tied-down mothers envied me and my freedom and my travels. I envied them; that was what mattered. I thought of the days when I used to say to other nurses, "No, sir, no family for mine. Footloose and fancy free, that's me." But now I wished I could burrow in to the heart of life and just live there contentedly, not aching. Maybe it was that I had served my apprenticeship at last. For me it was strange to be uncertain, not to be hot on some new job, some new place, some new exciting life. That night by the fire I half made up my mind that when I went away from Labrador I'd adopt a girl like Marjorie maybe, and try to pretend she was my own.

I took a bath then, because it rests me. The height of glory here, as in many parts of the world, is for a woman to say, "It was a terrible time. I never had my clothes off for eight days and nights!" I myself prefer a change and my two-pint bath of warm water in a pan by the stove because it rests me. After my scrub I curled up in my sleeping bag between the woodbox and the stove where I could handily put on a chunk each time I woke. The snow had stopped and it was growing colder.

So the days passed, each one showing an improvement. Mrs. Michelin had in three days picked up enough to be out of danger, but it would be weeks before she was strong enough to run the house. Evidently my diagnosis had been a little pessimistic, and the infection must have been more localized than I at first thought. Mrs. Michelin was worried that she had no milk, but now that her temperature had fallen and she was so much better, I began to reestablish the diminished milk supply, knowing its value to Harold's chances of survival. We are taught in Australia that in certain matters humans have not been able to improve on nature, and that there is nothing quite so fine as a breast-fed baby—all baby-food manufacturers to the contrary. Consequently breast feeding is a religion to Australian nurses and mothers. After unremitting work, lactation began, greatly to Mrs. Michelin's surprise. Harold was stronger now, and vigorous sucking would do the rest.

At the end of the five days when Jim came, I sent him to Mulligans for a relative of Mrs. Michelin's, a competent lass who soon caught on to the details of treatment. Marjorie's leg was so nearly clean and healed that in a day or so she would be out around, able to help Wesley with fishing and setting snares and hunting partridges. Harold was gaining steadily, and Mrs. Michelin was pleased with the flow of milk, which she somehow attributed to my arrival.

Early in the morning as usual, Jim was hitched up again, the empty komatik box, the medicine chest, the bags and caribou robes lashed on. "'Tis a mild we've got," he said.

Sure enough, the eaves were dripping, and we were in for one of those freakish thaws that sometimes gum up winter travel. Mrs. Michelin had cried a little bit. "Nonsense," I told her, "you're as good as well again."

"I know it," she said. "I feel so glad, but sad you're leavin'."

"Send a letter if someone passes by," I said, "and tell me how you are, how you really are. Don't tell me about the weather."

I left her smiling on the pillow. The children raised their little hands and looked so lonesome, standing in the doorway.

For a few miles the snow bore up our runners, and at sunrise, a beauty with oceans of colored cloud fields, we were a long way out on the bay. A blue haze crept over all the shores. The dogs began to sink, the runners stuck and great clogging lumps formed on the front of the sledge. It crunched slowly from length to length like an inch-worm measuring itself. We had to walk to lighten the load, and the walking was terrific with snowshoes on, and impossible without. When we left our first boil-up place, we each took with us a stick for knocking our snowshoes, but even so, they were heavy. Lifting that extra weight stretches a muscle in the thigh and gives one what the voyageurs used to call *mal de raquette*. Nobody knows how small a person seems and how big the bay, when the team crawls and the walking is heavy. You might as well set out walking to the moon as toward the next point. It was slow and we were sweating. We wished it were twenty below again so we could travel fast and be dry and comfortable. Three times we stopped for bread and tea, and each time the breeze seemed cold, our backs shivery, our feet clammy, our mittens soggy. At dusk the point of North West River was still four miles away. I walked it thinking of a warm bath and dry clothes and some tea, and maybe Jane would make me some cinnamon toast, and I'd pretend I was civilized, in slippers and a dressing gown, with a pillow for my head. Maybe another mail had come up the bay and there'd be letters. It seemed too much to hope.

We were crossing the beach, we were going through the portage path. The back of the hospital was in sight, we were seeing the yellow windows, the cheery lights of home.

I opened the door, and stood aghast. The big room was full of people waiting to see me. A baby was screaming. Murdock McLean got up from a bench and said, "I got a wonderful sick boy to home, Miss. We'd like it fine for you to come right now."

I looked around at the others. "How long has Clarence been sick, Murdock?"

"Two days now, and he has a fever, and pains all over."

Pearlie came running down the stairs. "Oh Miss, oh Miss, I got an Indian girl in bed up there that's dyin', I s'pose. Shakin' all over and don't wake up at all. She came in a hour ago and gets worse and worse all the time."

"All right, Pearlie. What ails the baby there that's crying so?"

It was Stuart Michelin's eighteen-months' boy, with, of all things, a bean up his nose. The nose was swollen, the bean was swollen, and it looked as though fourteen people had been experimenting with the situation. Beside the baby sat a boy named George Monroe from across the bay. His swollen eyes were streaming and he kept them tight shut even when he spoke. Snowblindness again.

The Indian girl sounded most pressing. I ran upstairs and found her quite unconscious, having convulsions. We'd have to hurry. I called Sarah Jane, Pearlie, Polly. "Bring up all the hot water you can. We'll put her in a hot pack." Three Indians stood by the bed. I moved them into a corner out of the way. My mind flew to an old textbook page that I could see as plain as day: an illustration of a nice white porcelain bathtub with faucets that ran hot or cold (imagine it!), and the words, "Convulsions—immerse patient in hot bath, cold pack on head, give enema at once."

"Get a history, Pearlie. Talk to them. What can they tell you? Do they know what ails her?" While they were speaking the Montagnais dialect, I decided it looked like a case of poison, so I gave the child a complete washout anyway. Then Polly and I rigged a bed with waterproof sheeting, fixed a blanket in a drawsheet and plunged it in the water.

"He says," said Pearlie, "that they've ate some bad deer meat and all been sick. But this is the sickest."

"I hope so," said Polly. She took an end, and together we wrung the blanket as dry as possible. Inside it we quickly wrapped the girl, covered her with more waterproofing and blankets, and packed hot-water bags around her. Then we put some bags of snow on her head. It's very easy to freeze or burn a patient in this process, so I took care of that. Gradually we began to get results. The convulsions grew less till they ceased, the eyes which had been squinting set straight, the child appeared to stir and then to sleep. Soon she opened her eyes and looked around. The three Indians came closer, to look at her. They glanced sidewise at me, serious as judges, making me feel spooky. They were wondering about my hot water and snow magic maybe.

All this took half an hour, but it must have seemed a long time to Murdock. I put on my dickie and mitts, and got aboard my snowshoes again. While we walked the short distance to his house he told me some more about Clarence. Murdock's wife, Mae, received me cordially, for we were good friends now. A quick examination, the swollen, reddened joints, the high temperature, convinced me it was rheumatic fever. Clarence was indeed very sick, and I wanted to take him back to the hospital right then, but they wouldn't consent. As long as there was nothing they couldn't do, they would keep him. Knowing so well how little there was to do, how little, but how important it was to keep him lying perfectly still, on a milk diet for weeks and weeks, I wondered if they could possibly manage it. It's when there is little to do that the care is hardest of all. Probably I didn't have the strength at the moment, or I should have insisted. So I went back to the hospital after promising to send fresh milk daily and such articles of diet as would help. For the hundredth time I blessed the mission cows. He'd have very little chance on bread and tea with a bit of pork and gravy.

At the hospital the Indian girl was almost normal, so I sent her companions away. When Pearlie brought Mrs. Stuart up with the boy, we flipped the mask over his face and gave him a few spots of ether to keep him quiet. The poor child, having suffered for over twenty-four hours, was almost exhausted from crying. I found the bean had softened, and that I could extract it piecemeal with forceps—a few minutes' work. He came to just long enough for opening his coal-black eyes, and then dropped his head on his mother's shoulder and fell asleep. We wrapped a blanket around him, and out into the night they went.

The last patient had fallen asleep too on his bench in the corner of the big room. We took him up to treat his swollen eyes. They were so bad I decided to keep him overnight at least. First an irrigation of boracic solution, then alternate hot and cold packs on the eyelids for an hour, some soothing oil drops, and finally George was more comfortable with a black bandage to exclude all light. We tucked him in and said good night.

It was an hour after midnight.

"My, Miss," said Sarah Jane, "you ain't even had a cup of tea yet. The kittle must a boiled dry long ago."

I seemed to remember something about cinnamon toast. "Make me some cinnamon toast, would you, Sarah Jane?"

"And look at you," said Pearlie. "You ain't even got off your wet travelin' pants."

"Maybe you didn't know," Polly said, "that the mail's in."

So I had my bath and my moment of luxury at last, dressing gown, cinnamon toast, five cups of tea, letters and all. I was so sleepy I read only one. It was summertime in Australia now, and the jacaranda trees were in flower. My dear Aunt Myrna wanted to know, "How ever do you pass the time in that godforsaken place?"

SNOWSHOE TRAIL

OWARD THE BEGINNING OF FEBRUARY some score of trappers in the village of North West River, Labrador, begin to tighten their belts and figuratively clench the muscles of their jaws. They have been home from the woods for the three-weeks midwinter sojourn. Now it is time to start up the frozen rivers on the bitterest trip of the year, the long haul back to the distant furring grounds.

It is a little like going to war. Each man is conscious of an enormous Presence that begins just back of the houses, the wilderness that is waiting. He hates it and loves it, he fears it and defies it, and understands its grimness and its bounty. His utmost endurance, his fortitude that is a steel-strong habit in the long days, will not change its sphinx-like face by so much as an ice crystal. But in the mystery of paradoxical sensations that the wilderness rouses each man feels that he has been made whatever he is by the great Unknowable where he is going. It cares not whether it kills him or makes him rich, but he is close enough to the great Unknowable to have borrowed and armed himself with a little of its own immortal carelessness.

Henry Blake and I and a man named Edward Michelin were together most of the way up, seventeen days of the most abominable weather that ever was; thaws, rains, blizzards, and gales of wind at thirty below.

We were bound up Grand River (now the Churchill) on the

spring hunt, early February to mid-April, for a point some two hundred miles west of the head of Hamilton Inlet. Henry's fur paths and cabin were at the upper end of Lake Winokapau and once there he had promised to teach me as much as he could about trapping. Edward was going fifty miles farther on. Both men were native trappers of European stock, crossed in the time of their great-grandfathers with Eskimo.

Some weeks before this my wife and I had reached the village after four months in the bush with trappers. On that trip we left in September before the freeze-up and in our deep, strong canoes built especially for the rapids were able to take a considerable supply of grub. But this time everything had to be lashed on toboggans, and my dog and I could scarcely haul enough to nourish ourselves. Kate had to stay with our friends, the Groves, at Goose Bay, a day's walk from the village. She learned to knit trout nets, hunted and fished, tried her hand at making caribou-skin moccasins, did a little nursing when anyone within reach was so kind as to be sick, read again the finest book in all the world, *Jean Christophe* by Romain Rolland. The monotony of the long winters is something that persistently eluded both of us.

For this, the spring hunt, Ed had a catamaran (a light sledge with wide runners) and a powerful husky dog to help him. Henry had a toboggan and a little Indian hunting dog named Dash. Dash was very small, but if the going was not too bad he could haul a small bundle of clothes and a grub bag done up in a sealskin. I had a toboggan for myself and another small one for my dog. She followed along behind on the track, or was supposed to. My dog's name was Diamond, but before we got home again she was so thin, poor thing, that Henry called her Old Drybones.

With the varying weather we had all kinds of going, crust that broke and hooked our snowshoes, light, powdery snow in which we sank above the knees with our racquets on, but most of all sticky snow that clung to the snowshoes, making them weigh about ten pounds apiece, and put the brakes on our sleds till we could barely move them. Sometimes they came so hard it seemed as though we were just rocking from side to side in pain and not stepping ahead at all. We'd start out in the morning and it would be such hard hauling I'd say to myself a man can't keep this up all day no matter who he is. And in the evening we'd still be at it.

Labradormen are odd with their code of never giving in. Most

every evening about half past four we'd stagger up a bank, build a
fire and boil a kettle of tea. After we were finished, we'd start picking up our grub bags while Henry said, "Well, I s'pose we better go
on a ways," and Edward answered, "Sure."

Then casually looking around he would remark that it looked
like a pretty good place to camp. Henry would say, "Yes, it is a
pretty good place for wood and brush." Then they'd both turn to
me and ask me if I wanted to go on or camp.

I joined in the farce always and said, "It's up to you. I don't care.
I'd just as soon go on if you want." Really I didn't see how I could
crawl another inch, but I've found you always can somehow, especially after a cup of tea.

Then Henry or Ed (generally they alternated, one tonight and
the other tomorrow) would say, "Well, I aren't tired, but if you fellus
want to we may's well camp'er down. My! we've only come a little
piece today."

Up by Mouni's Rapid I got snowblind. My glasses were fancy
things from the States with sides in them and fur to go against the
face. Of course they steamed up from the warmth of my face inside
and the cold outside. I got disgusted and took them off. The third
evening the blindness struck me. I was almost totally blind for one
day and blind in one eye for three days. It was a very mild attack,
but the light from a candle in the opposite corner of the tent would
stab me through the head like a knife, even though I had my eyes
covered with a bandanna and my two hands. A pair of "glasses"
such as the Eskimos have used for centuries would have been
much better. They are pieces of wood about an inch thick, carved
the shape of eyeglasses. They are pierced by two tiny eye holes. The
outer part of each hole is cut away, funnel shape, to enlarge the
range of vision. The sides of the funnels are blackened with
charred wood to dull the light that enters to the eyes.

It was a February of unprecedented mildness. The river was
open almost everywhere along by Mouni's. We crossed on a rotten
bridge of ice, tapping ahead of us with sticks. Now and then the
stick went through and we stepped elsewhere. The bridge disinte-
grated as we walked on it. I doubt if anyone could have crossed
behind us. Next morning it was gone.

Ed left us there to go on up to his place at the Big Hill. We had to
stop a day and a half to look at some traps Henry had left set by the
river in December on his way home.

Our last day up that interminable Lake Winokapau there was a crust on top and sticky snow underneath. At every step we broke through a hole nearly two feet deep and could hardly pull our racquets out to make another hole. We took fifteen-minute turns ahead. At the end of each period the man who had been breaking trail would sit on his sled gasping and rubbing his legs while the sweat ran into his eyes and the shivers coursed up and down his back. The other fellow went on, punching holes in the crust, floundering, stumbling, often falling, beating his snowshoes with a stick at each step to knock the lumps off them. It was easy enough to catch up to him, and then came the turn ahead again. If we took off our snowshoes we sank almost to the hip and the bottom six inches was water on the ice. The hauling lines ate into our arms and chafed our hands raw in the mittens.

For hours we never spoke, afraid of the words of weakness we might say if we opened our lips. Henry's sled had one crossbar broken off and it was running badly. He was also suffering from indigestion. I was ahead for a long stretch and I commenced to leave him behind. When two men are traveling under such terrific stress, it unfortunately but almost inevitably becomes a contest with considerable temporary bitterness. I know that it is so with Labradorman and Labradorman. Perhaps it is even more so with a Labradorman and an outsider. I cannot explain it; nevertheless, the feeling is tremendously powerful. As I commenced to draw away I looked back and saw that Henry was pale and had his teeth in his lip. A gust of blinding passion shook the sanity right out of me and I thought as my teeth ground savagely, "Now I can leave you if I want. You have left me behind so many times on these sled hauling trips, all you Labradormen; you have always been superior, now it is my turn for once. Ah, God, I don't care if his sled is running harder than mine and he's sick. I wouldn't care if he had a broken leg. No one has ever cared if I was lame and my load was lashed on crooked and my hands were freezing. It's a fight and nothing counts but results. I can leave him, I can leave him. I don't care why, the fact remains."

I had no intention of leaving him or even showing him that I could. It was only the glory of knowing that I could, that I had the power. I could have held up my fists to the sky and screamed with evil joy. I did not remember how Henry and others like him have taught me and hauled stuff for me to make my load lighter and waited for me and been kind to me in the midst of the cruelest suffering. For a moment there was not one spark of goodness in me. I found myself trembling and afraid.

Henry hauled up alongside and we stopped and ate bread and sugar to keep us going. After that he was as good for it as I was.

All afternoon the same stony headlands looked down on us, two specks in a pit of mountains. They eyed us, as distant and unattainable as the clouds. Poor Diamond commenced to falter and drop way behind on the track. I put more of her load on my sled. When she got a quarter of a mile back she would lie down in the snow and stay there. I had to run back and get her and drive her ahead of me and try to catch up. When I had caught up it would be time for my turn ahead again and I was so done out from running I could hardly stagger.

At nine o'clock, hours and hours after dark we reached Henry's cabin, which is built in a level grove of birches close to the shore at the foot of a mountain. The mountain looks as though it would one day kick the cabin into the lake. But for a protecting spur of rock, avalanches would have done so long ago. We dug out the door and went in. For a minute we sat in the cold dark with our heads in our hands not thinking of anything, not even of lighting a fire in the tin camp stove. We were too tired to cook the meal of bacon and peas we would have liked, but after a mugup of bread and tea it was fine to curl down in the bag and pull the soft duffle blanket up close and drop off to sleep with the friendly fire snapping and the light from the damper hole dancing black and gold on the logs.

IN THE DAYLIGHT the huge thirty-five-mile lake with its jagged edge of sheer blue mountains rising to the sky made that cabin seem too small even to exist. The weight of the mountains and the length of the lake crushed its being, its consciousness of itself to absolute nothing. Sometimes at dusk I would be coming home across the lake. Perhaps Henry was at the cabin skinning fur and had the candle lit. It used to make me smile—the crouched, menacing bulk of the mountain, like a black giant as high as the sky, and perched on one of his toenails, the cocky pinpoint light, laughing.

Henry furred the path that goes into the country three days' walk to the south and I furred the trapline that extends three days to the north. He took me with him once in each path setting up traps and trying to teach me as much as he could in the short time. Then we went our separate ways in opposite directions, always arranging, however, to meet on Saturdays or Sundays at the cabin by the lake.

The north path was all long narrow lakes and hills, a chopped up, broken country of woods and open ice and long views over endless trees and snowy land. About every quarter of a mile there would be a trap. Setting and baiting and fixing them barehanded is cold work. The smell of the rotten fish and beaver castor bait never left me. Otter and beaver traps are the coldest to manage, for they are set in water. It's very strange and illuminating to be alone in the woods 150 miles from a living soul, with darkness coming on, not knowing the way very well, the wind rising and the sky aching to belch snow. All nature seems to be brooding, watching. It makes you very careful of your feet when you see the shiny axe blade bite the wood you're cutting up for the night. Sometimes the atmosphere was so hostile, I had no idea of ever getting out of it alive, but I wasn't really afraid.

One of those lowering, hostile days I had to stop all day at the little tilt on a hillside by a lake that Henry calls Red Water. Diamond was having puppies. Three little beauties they were, two brown and white and one black and white like herself. I had a heavy pack and no sled. They couldn't walk and I couldn't carry them. Diamond was so thin I doubt if she could have fed them long. We had nothing to feed them on and very little for ourselves and Diamond. We couldn't haul them two hundred miles down the river and care for them all the way. I had to kill them, though I would almost as soon have killed myself. I took Diamond down the hill to the shore and tied her to a tree; then hurried back up, and laying the puppies' heads on a log, I smashed them with an axe handle. I looked up, shivering, smeared with blood, and there stood Diamond silent between two trees watching. She had slipped her harness. *The Hound of the Baskervilles* flashed into my mind. I don't know why. I suppose because the story sickened me with horror when I read it at the age of twelve. Diamond didn't fly at my throat. I took her down the hill again and tied her fast with trembling fingers, then buried the pups a long way off in the snow. I think I know the grisly feeling of being a murderer, a Macbeth or an explorer who shoots the dogs that have slaved for him. If a horned owl had called, I think I would have been off the handle.

After all, confidence comes when the strangeness wears off.

There were sunny days too, swinging down narrow, cliff-bordered lakes for some of which I invented names each time I came to them, Rabbit Ribs, Paradise Alley, Hour-Glass, Puddle, Hole-in-the-Clouds, Shuttle, Never End. There were brooks where the water never stopped singing down under the ice and a beautiful hill above a fair-sized stream that I think was Michikamau River. Those days I forgot to remember blizzards and was glad to see nothing in the traps, dreaming all day to the snowshoe rhythm of old friends and when I was a kid and how Father used to read us *Robin Hood* and *Roland* and I used to look forward to it all day. At night the cozy fire and the northern lights and the bursting sensation of being tired and young and strong, absolutely on one's own to live or die. Funny to think I was once a brisk young man in an office.

We had a cold bright spell that lasted nearly two weeks during which the snowshoeing was perfect—a good crust with an inch-deep carpet of soft snow on top. The familiar webs that had grown so much a part of me seemed to have a spring of their own as though the day could never be long enough. I often used to stop on a hillside to look back at the trail streaming from my heels, flowing back astern, scarring the lonely, limitless snow as a ship's wake might scar the Pacific. Over glistening white hills and marshes and lakes it winds, a darker serpentine ribbon, scallop-edged, filled with tumbled blue shadow markings. And every individual print is a beautiful thing, a bit of sculpture, endless impressions of an Indian craftsman's masterpiece. Here is the broader webbed *babische* of the close-knit middles, here the finer knit *tibische* of the heads and tails molded into the snow, perfect in every finest line; there the round-curved frame of strong white birch and the lip of the tail, the head bar and the tail bar, the toe hole and a small cup scooped from the snow where my toe pushed through the hole at the end of the step; the blurred mark of the dragging tail, then another perfect, graceful-lined pattern printed in blue-white marble.

Sunny days something seemed to be pulling me along, calling to me. It was never this tree, this drifted-up brook under the silver pines, this willow twig right here. It was always on, on through the bright quiet country, beyond the lakes and over the spruce ridges that leaned against the sky far ahead. I found myself wondering what it was, this persistent call that I could not answer. And at last

I became convinced that it was not just fancy, but something concrete and real. It is happiness calling, "Come and take me if you are strong enough."

Evenings, after the wood was cut up and supper cooked and eaten, there was always the work of thawing and skinning fur, baking for tomorrow, mending snowshoes and getting everything ready for the start at daylight. I never stretched out on the log bunk before eleven o'clock or midnight. Then the cold woke me up to stoke the stove two or three times before dawn. In the path one can carry neither blanket nor sleeping bag.

We were short of grub most of the time and seldom killed all the partridge, rabbits, or porcupine we wanted. There was some old caribou track. Occasionally we managed to get enough meat for a big feed that would satisfy our hunger. Especially for Sundays at the big cabin by the lake we tried to do this. But in general the mainstay was bannock and not enough of that. I tried to bake about half what I knew I'd want. The brain keeps saying, "If you don't skimp you'll starve altogether," and the stomach answers, "Let's eat and the devil with tomorrow."

THE SECOND OF APRIL we pulled out for home. My total was five mink, three marten, and twenty-five ermine. Very poor.

Henry had to haul home the canoe that he came up the river in last fall. A couple of days before we left he cut down a straight-grained spruce and hewed out a catamaran sledge to drag the canoe on. Winokapau was sticky again and it took us a day and a half to get to the lower end, Henry, the dog, and I all hauling on the catamaran, with my toboggan, the sleeping bags, tent and stove, guns, kettles and grub all piled in the canoe. Below the lake the river was open for a long way. It was sunset when we got to the water, put the catamaran aboard and started walking down the current with our arms instead of over the ice with our legs. Before the long twilight was over the swift tide had bowled us down to Mouni's, a distance that took us three days on the way up.

Ten miles below Mouni's we paddled next day before we came to the ice. In the afternoon in a snowstorm we met Victor Goudie and Gordon Goudie, two young fellows with a dog team and komatik on their way up to get their canoes and bring them down for next fall's hunt again. As prearranged they brought two dogs for us.

We hauled where the river was frozen and paddled wherever there was a mile or so of open water. In many places the ice was covered with water and getting weak. Our sealskin boots were leaky and getting worn out too. Places where the ice was bending under us we'd run along with one hand on the canoe so that we could hold on and it would float us at any minute if the whole business went through. We hauled across lots of yellow, slushy places we wouldn't have dared try but for our amphibian rig. Generally when we were in the canoe we let the dogs follow along shore.

We nearly got a ducking in the Horseshoe Rapids. It was sleeting and freezing on us as we paddled down toward them, the water very black and filled with floating slob, the hills lost in slanting snow, the canoe and everything in it draped with wet, white flakes, such a vague, strange, magic, miserable afternoon. I looked back at Henry in the stern, covered with snow, a fur cap, ragged beard, icy mitts on an icy paddle; sliding down that black river he looked the picture of an oldtime voyageur. We had three rapids to run before we got to Horseshoe tilt, a cabin tucked away beside a brook in a deep valley of enormous hills. Down ahead the rapids were roaring and the broad water narrowed to a raging channel between sheer ten-foot walls of blue and green ice. We picked up speed until it seemed we were falling through this chasm. Ahead of us the water broke at the brink of the rapid's slant. The incline was so steep we couldn't see over to make out where the worst rocks or the smoothest water lay.

We were rushing down the grade when we saw about fifty yards ahead of us the big white plume that curls up over a boulder just under the surface. We dug our paddles to get clear, but an eddy drew us right down on it. At the last second Henry stuck her straight for it, because if she hit broadside, she would roll over and over like a barrel. We were flying and the water looked very cold. Just above the rock there was a deep pocket where the water dipped and then flew into the air over the rock. Into this hole we plunged, stood almost straight on end, put the bow right under and filled the canoe a quarter full. But she rose to it ever so quickly and we shot up over the boulder and never touched. We must have had an inch or so to spare. We spent the night at Horseshoe tilt and I was glad, for I was freezing.

From there on it was all ice. We were up before sunrise every morning, watching the weather like cats, hating the warm sun that came at noon to rot the crust, hating the rain or the snow or the east wind because they were our enemies that chained our feet and slowed the sleds. Mostly we had sunny days and our faces were burned nearly black with the glare from the snow. In those long spring days of five o'clock dawn and eight o'clock dark we made thirty-five mile runs.

The last morning I was glad when I parted from Henry at Traverspine to cut across the six miles of woods for Goose Bay and Kate. Then I could limp as much as I wanted. I was crusted with dirt, ragged, hungry, my sled was broken and patched, my dog was as lean as a fence rail and most of all I was weary with the cumulative weariness of walking, hauling, running, paddling, cooking, getting wood and water, patching boots for endless days and nights. The last few days there had been no beauty in nature, only adverse or advantageous traveling conditions. The great high hills beside the river half lost in snowstorms, the lovely purple snow that sparkles with gold dust in the sunrise, the blue sky and sunset clouds were very little to me compared with a good crust that would get us along. Getting along—that is the fixed idea, waking and sleeping. All for a dream of comfort and food and relief from walking, walking, walking. It wasn't all quite crushed out of me, but almost. I was good and sick of the life in the woods and could hardly bear the thought of ever going up the river again.

And then all at once I was home again. Clean clothes and comfort and leisure, days and nights of luxurious aches in a bottomless abyss of sleep, much food, and the depths of the abyss once more. The world of books and thoughts again. I had forgotten it. The world of quiet sunsets through the window and the snowy mountains deepening, darkening. No more of the knife-like keenness of self-preservation, no more lean endless strength set in endless weariness. A house was like a fort, safe even from storms, a place to be secure in, and being secure, at peace.

It bothered me considerably in the last few days to see my long-tried philosophy going to pot. But there in the house I remembered that the swing of contrasting cycles, Labradormen have told me, is much the same with them. Toward the end of the summer, living with their families in their snug houses by the shore of the bay, they begin to grow restless for the absolute freedom of their solitary fur paths way off in the country. In the silence and the snow there will be no one to consider but themselves. There will be no one to get hungry or sick or cold, no one to slow them up, no one to make concessions to or expect help from. A hunter works alone, supreme and free, sufficient unto himself in the life he knows and understands.

But by the time the winter is over each man is tired of the silence, hating the smell of balsam bed, sick to the soul of walking and hauling, mending snowshoes, skinning fur, partridge stew, the dirt, the hardship. He starts on the long haul home "drivin' 'er," and he keeps it up to unbelievable limits of endurance. On the bad ice, across sticky lakes where the crust is rotten, in the glare of the high spring sun on blinding whiteness the image of home sustains him. Home means a spot that he picked himself where the water is deep to the shore and boats can float in to the bank, a clearing that he made with his own axe, a house that he raised with his own hands and has been fighting for ever since. Several times a year he tumbles into his own little nest, ragged, dirty, utterly weary, unquenchably hungry, "done." It is too good to be true.

For both the man and his woman, who is a most indispensable partner with him in the business of living, existence is a long round of contrasts. At least twice a year they have the good fortune to be separated. The man leaves the village bound into the country and they part with a casual "So long," or "Good luck." The woman turns back to the house and the children and waits and works hard and is cold and afraid some nights. But at last it is over once more. One afternoon a chain of black specks appears far out on the ice. The children run down to the shore and yell, "Paa's comin'." The woman gets out the glass and steadying it on the window sill looks long. By the time the links of the chain are as big as peas she knows by the gait and the swing of the arms if her man is there. The travelers come up the bank, and even their stained, frayed clothing looks weary. The children proudly take the sled and the man straightens up and walks to his house. He is home and his woman is feeding him and each of them knows that the other has been a bit of a hero just by living his life. Nothing is ever wearisome.

I am thankful to have been a little part of this, to know the ever newness of such a way of life. And more than all is the land, the backdrop against which these lives are tempered, taught, crushed, made strong or beautiful. The long white lakes, the mountains and rivers, the space and the northern lights, the spruce forests and birch hills, the cold and the terrible beauty of it when darkness is tightening like a grip of iron; nothing in my lifetime will be more satisfying to have glimpsed than the heart of all that.

HE SAILED AWAY

**P**ARSON WORTHINGTON taught the Eskimos many things during his three-year stay at Tikujak-vak. Then the fourth time his supply schooner came into the harbor he sailed away never to return. His converts stood on the cliffs with tears in their eyes and rocked their bodies to and fro in sorrow, even after the schooner's sails had dropped below the horizon. But he left behind him the barrel organ he had brought and taught them to play, and that reconciled them. Gradually they returned to their old life, but it was never quite the same. . . .

There had been no permanent settlement at Tikujakvak until Parson Worthington came. Some stone huts centuries old stood on a patch of grass beneath the towering cliffs. The harbor, which to a white man looked chillingly desolate and forbidding, was a well-known Eskimo camping place, for walrus were to be found among the outer islands at certain seasons, the wide harbor was a favorite sealing ground, there were fish in the waters and duck eggs in niches of the cliffs.

Sometimes, in the early summer, five tents of reindeer skin were pitched beside the brook, facing seaward toward the white bergs that drifted gently by from north to south. Sometimes in the winter dark, ten igloos cowered in the drifts below the cliffs, and sometimes none. Often in late summer the cup-shaped harbor was alone; the cliffs mirrored themselves in black water uncut by a kayak's prow, the seaweed on the rocks closed and opened its fronds with the swell, while the gurgling of the ocean and the screaming of the gulls were the only sounds.

In autumn when the pools among the rocks were skimmed with new ice a family or two came down the slantwise path to the beach, burdened with packs, their dogs too saddled with skins and belongings. Perhaps a summer storm had cast up driftwood, and a sledge was made. The population of Tikujakvak appeared from out of the vast nowhere, and melted again into the nowhere. They were nomads scouring the barrens for reindeer, and the mountains for musk ox, hunting the blue fox, traveling on and on. Their komatik runners marked hundreds of miles of coastline and the double ribbons of their track streamed across inland plateaus and sea-ice straits. The edges of the world were their home. The northern lights, which are the spirits of still-born babies, streak the sky even to the south of them.

Parson Worthington's advent changed their habits. He was one of the earliest religious pioneers in that land and the language gave him great difficulty. But he had brought with him Eskimo dictionaries compiled by Danish explorers. His parishioners also taught him, word by word, since he found their dialect quite different from that of the dictionaries. He rose early and lived Spartanly and toiled ceaselessly. Gradually he was able to tell them of the Bible and of Christ and of God.

The Eskimos drank in his teachings as a sponge drinks water. They helped him to build a little church of the ancient huts of stone. Two driftwood poles that were to have been a sledge with crossbars of bone, became a cross of Christ at the top of the cliff. They learned that people who do not go to church do not go to Heaven. Sinners go to a land of burning fire and hunger and thirst called Hell. And so the settlement beside the church grew larger, until the little church could scarcely hold its flock.

When the supply of game for fifty miles around had been depleted, hunger made itself felt, and the children whimpered with their empty bellies. But the hunters dared not be absent from the church for very long. The women complained that there were no new furs with which to edge their hoods and trim their clothing. The reindeer robes on the benches of their igloos became worn and hairless, and there were no more. But the hunters feared the place called Hell, and the parson told them their souls were of more importance than their clothing or their stomachs.

Parson Worthington found them a friendly, childish people. Most of the men had muzzle-loader guns which they had bought with furs from a whaling ship that had touched those shores. There were a few highly prized steel knives, and the women had some steel needles, worn short, but of incalculable value. Parson Worthington gave them some more needles, provided they did not use them on Sunday. He also procured for them new supplies of powder and shot, which advanced his prestige among them more than he knew. He was surprised that they were so fond of dancing and laughing. "I think," he wrote to his Bishop, "I have never seen so laughing, so happy a people." He did not need to fear them. It was long after his time that traders murdered several Eskimos of the district and subsequent traders who were fortunate enough to escape being murdered on sight sent out to the world stories of a blood-thirsty race. On the whole, he concluded, they were practically untouched by civilization.

Parson Worthington painfully translated for them the hymns, "Rock of Ages," "Old Hundred," "Jesus Savior Pilot Me," and "Blood of the Lamb." And these the Eskimos learned aptly, rapturously. They swayed to the rhythms with barbarous ecstasy and their slanting black eyes sparkled with one of the greatest joys, the joy of music. The same harmony, the same chords that have shaken the rafters of New England meeting houses for generations, resounded in the harbor of Tikujakvak.

There was a matter which Parson Worthington could never learn the language well enough to explain. He lived alone in a hut of boards which was walled around the outside with blocks of snow to keep it warm in winter. He stoked his own little coal stove and cooked his own meals and swept his own floor. All this he did, shameful though it was, but he could not sew the skin of the fox and the caribou and the wolverene, he could not make his own sealskin boots and his mittens and his hooded capote, much less ornament them as a great man's clothing should be ornamented. That the chief man of a band must beg other men's wives to sew his clothing is a disgrace to all concerned. Moreover, he must be lonely and cold at night on his solitary bench. The father of the settlement's most beautiful girl proudly offered his daughter. The parson could have her for his own as long as she pleased him. If, after a time, he cast her off, the distinction of having once been the pastor's wife would bring her many new suitors. Her contemporaries remarked the honor that was in store, in the same way that they remarked the novelty of her blue eyes and gold hair. Long, long ago in 1579 one of her forgotten great-great-great-grandmothers had pleased a sailor of Sir Martin Frobisher's crew.

But the parson's strength was as the strength of ten and he graciously declined. Nevertheless, the unalterable fact remained that it was a refusal. The parents could see it in no other light and they were insulted, and the poor girl herself was an object of ridicule. She could scarcely hold up her head.

During the summer of his second year a strange and unknown malady afflicted the community, which had by now grown to a hundred souls. It was a form of dysentery and it carried off seven children and so weakened dozens of adults that they could only lie in their tents and groan, or creep about on hands and knees. Parson Worthington cared for his sufferers tenderly and administered to them some bitter stuff which he called quinine, but which did them no good; until he himself was stricken. Then Saipaudok cared for him, and it was because Saipaudok was there to bring a drink of water whenever the parson called for it, to feed him weak broth and make his tea and put sugar in it, that Parson Worthington did not die.

Gradually the parson recovered his strength and took up again the daily lessons with Saipaudok. For Saipaudok was now his right-hand man and most promising pupil. It had not taken long to see that Saipaudok was the most intelligent native in the settlement. In the old hunting days he had been leader of a clan of four families, and the best hunter in the memory of those now living. His family seldom wanted for meat, his wives left to rot all but the finest skins, for they had plenty of the finest. His kayak was the swiftest; he would paddle into a herd of walrus and harpoon one of the monsters with no more fear than a boy who catches a hare in his snare. His dogs were the fleetest. His arm was the strongest. Once, in a time of great hunger he had chased caribou four days and four nights, without food and almost without rest, until he ran them down. It was even said that when he was a young man he had traveled to another land far toward the sinking of the sun, a land so far distant that its mountains lifted their shoulders from the ice only after eight days' journeying.

This man gave up his hunting to become Parson Worthington's most promising convert. He taught Parson Worthington sufficient

fluency to preach simple sermons. He became Parson Worthington's intermediary with the people. It was he whom the parson sent
to tell his people that they must clean up the refuse that littered the
shores, that it was because of the stinking seal carcasses and fish
heads and bones and entrails that the sickness had smote them.
But in this commission the faithful Saipaudok was not successful.
It is impossible to change all the habits of centuries at once. "What
need is there?" the people asked. "Soon we will travel away to a
new place, as we have always done, where meat is plentiful in winter and the stones have no smell. We have been here too long. The
parson will come with us."

"Never mind, my brother," the parson said to Saipaudok. "You
have done your best. When I am well we will tidy up the shore and
make the place more wholesome." And they did try. But the most
rudimentary ideas of community sanitation were foreign to this
nomadic people. It was a good summer for seals and for fish. The
bones and the entrails and the fish heads flew out of the tent flaps
as always and lay where they fell. Seal carcasses rotted on the
beach, and the dogs and the gulls could not eat them all. Children
played in filth and tracked it about. The stench was strong and the
buzzing of the bloated flies sounded louder than the gurgle of swell
against the rocks.

The settlement was so hopelessly dirty that Parson Worthington
would gladly have loaded himself with the women and dogs and
chattels into one of the large sealskin umiaks and paddled off,
while the men accompanied them in their swifter kyaks, hunting
as they went. But there was the church, and the organ. And he
could not carry his necessities of life. Moreover, once they started
traveling again, there was no telling where they might go to in this
vast and almost unknown land. An adverse wind, a broken sledge,
an early breakup, poor or exceptionally fine hunting, any one of a
thousand unpredictable happenings would surely prevent his
return to the harbor at an exact date to meet his yearly supply
ship. "I must not value my life too highly," he said. "I am but a servant of God." And yet, if he missed the supply ship he would die,
for he could not live on meat and fish exclusively as his children
could. And if he died, this nucleus of Christianity that he had produced would die also. So the settlement of Tikujakvak stayed
where it was.

Autumn came, the miserable time of wind and sleet when the

tents cannot be kept warm and the snow is not deep enough and the drifts are not hard enough for cutting igloo blocks.

And then in the early winter it happened.

Saipaudok and four of the best hunters set off early one morning for the blowholes three miles along shore in a cove of giant boulders. There they would stand all day, tirelessly alert, ready with their oonocks and their coiled sealskin lines to harpoon a seal as it came up to breathe. The seals kept these holes at the Cove of Boulders open all winter. Even after the ice grew four feet thick the air holes were still open. For a seal must breathe every twenty minutes or he drowns. But the wary seals have many breathing holes and the hunter must be very quiet, very still, or his prey will go elsewhere. In any case the whiskered nose shows but for a second and is gone again in the twinkling of an eye.

The men were harnessing their teams, to ride as they always did. "No," said Saipaudok. "A dream has come to me. The seal spirits are frightened by the dog spirits. Better hunting will reward our walking." It was unusual.

"Later our dogs will draw home what little meat we may perhaps be fortunate enough to kill," he added modestly.

Hunters are not unaccustomed to the power of luck. So they walked, following around the shore in single file, Saipaudok bringing up the rear instead of leading.

When they had gone some little way Saipaudok took his oonock and his muzzle-loader in his left hand. Stealthily he drew his knife. He plunged it into the back before him, an oonock transfixed the next man, and as the third turned a shot blew a hole in him. Saipaudok was upon the leader like a cat, knocked up his gunbarrel and clubbed him senseless. The man died with a surprised look on his face. It had been done like lightning, and it had not been easy. But a hunter whose single spear slays the white bear can do much. Now they would all go to Heaven and be with the great king, God, in a land where there was much dancing and plenty of meat, and never any cold or pain. It was good that they should go quickly from this sinful place of toil and misery and the danger of Hell to that happy land. He, Saipaudok, had sped them, and it was well. They were the best hunters and the most worthy to go. Even now perhaps they were there, in their home behind the sky.

He returned to the village, went straight to the parson's hut and modestly told of his deed. The parson gasped, was stricken dumb, then began to babble a prayer. Saipaudok's youngest wife came in and asked in her rapid tongue why he had come home from the hunting alone. He told her. Terror swept her face.

"Their sons and brothers will kill you," she wept. "Quick, quick, harness the dogs while there is time."

He silenced her. "Shall Saipaudok, the hunter, flee from a pack of boys?"

Already a footstep squeaked on the snow outside. Saipaudok went out. "I shot your father," he said. "I speared, I clubbed, I knifed the others, and they are gone to the happy land, Heaven."

The man screamed with rage and grief. "And what of my mother and my sisters and the little ones?" he shouted, his eyes starting from his head. "Can I feed them?"

People were running, the village was in an uproar and the bereaved son kept on shouting. Saipaudok stood quietly by. Men with guns came up. They listened, and Saipaudok read the purpose in their eyes. The crowd murmured angrily, and children skipped out from behind him. He held his arms to the sky, opened his eyes wide and said in a clear singsong, "The God, she is my saver." And five guns roared almost at once and he fell.

That winter Parson Worthington hardly preached at all. He wandered a great deal alone on the barrens, miles back from the cliffs, and once in a blizzard in the time of twilight days he would have been lost had the Eskimos not saved him.

When his schooner came in the summer, he gave all his supplies to the dead men's families, and he sailed away. He dropped below the sharp rim of the sea to a land so far away he might have been dropping to another planet.

But he left his barrel organ. And for many years when scattered families came out of the vast nowhere and down the path by the cliff to camp on the beach at Tikujakvak for the walrus hunt or the salmon fishing, they danced to the barrel organ and to the hymns he had taught them.

THE LONE WOLF

IN FRONT OF THE CABIN old bones, old chips, one of his brother's worn-out boots, and a broken ax helve were emerging from a snowbank. It was lonely, somehow, seeing so many signs of man and no man. A warm south wind, sweet as a caress, came down the valley of the great river, stirring the spruces round the clearing, making him feel lonelier than ever.

It was Labrador springtime when the iron-white cold gentles to colored warmth. But Jan McKenzie only spat. He was still a hundred and fifty miles from home, and here was the river open, no ice shelf by the shore, nothing but the black current splotched with floating ice pans. From his furring grounds far up the river, he had walked this far, jarring step by jarring step. He could walk till he dropped, but now there was nothing to walk on.

Jan's left arm, bound with rags and splints of spruce, hung in a dirty sling made of canvas flour bag. The break, just below the elbow, was badly inflamed. Twice he had tried to set it straight, but he kept fainting and had had to give it up. It was set crooked he knew, because he could feel the bone ends grate.

Now Jan was paying for his lone-wolfishness. There was nobody else in all the four-hundred-mile length of Caribou River. The other trappers, whose cabins emphasized the river's solitude at thirty- or forty-mile intervals, were gone home. Only Jan had remained way up at his trapping grounds, as he always did, for the

59

spring muskrat hunting. Other men said, "The devil with spring muskrats. Five months in the woods is long enough." And onto their toboggans they lashed their winter's haul of fur and what little grub they had left, and traveled down the frozen river, hallooing at each lonely cabin, "Come on, b'y, bound fer home," till there were six or eight of them traveling together, taking turns at breaking trail, and swapping yarns at night. They were weary with months on the trap lines, and they couldn't be bothered hauling home the canoes that had carried their supplies upriver in the fall. Next autumn was a long way off, and they'd build or buy a new one when that time came.

So if Jan was late and the breakup early, there was no lack of canoes by those deserted cabins. But how could he paddle with a broken arm?

He'd paddle somehow. Cautiously he got up, cradling his bad arm in his good, and went to look at Samson's canoes. There were three of them, all pretty old. He decided upon the smallest. Into it he tossed a coil of quarter-inch Manila tracking line that looked rather worn, but it might come handy in the rapids. Samson couldn't kick about this. He'd be glad to have one of his canoes brought down. He'd probably say, "Why didn't you tow the other two?" Be just like him.

Years ago they'd had a row, brother Samson claiming that a bag of flour was missing from his cabin one season after Jan passed by and everybody else was home from the river. There had been no definite accusation, but Jan considered the mere implication an insult. Since then, on the long hard journeys to and from his hunting grounds, Jan never slept in anybody's cabin but his own. No matter how late at night or how stormy and cold, he pitched his tent, chopped his wood, and depended upon himself solely. On nights when it was forty below he had been known to set up his tent and stove beside a cabin, carefully bank the canvas walls with snow and sleep there, within ten feet of comfort. Since the year that Samson lost his precious flour bag, Jan did not speak to him when they passed on the path at the village.

Daylight came again, and Jan was ready. There wasn't anything to put to rights in the cabin because he hadn't used anything of Samson's, not even the water bucket or the stove poker. In the corner back of the tin stove there was more dry kindling than there'd been before, though it had taken an hour to split it. Jan's grub was running short, but he wasn't taking any of Samson's, not if he starved for it. He hadn't even looked into the bags and grub boxes under the bunk.

He packed his gear aboard and shoved off through the tinkling thin ice of the cove. White mist, chilling and weird, rose from the black water. His heart beat, his arm throbbed. His clothes were damp, and his teeth began to chatter. For many days he had been unable to remove his shirt, sweater, or coat. Funny how handy two hands were, and you didn't know till you had only one. Dressing yourself, building fires, chopping wood, cooking, mixing dough, tying knots, hauling a sled, and now paddling—everything was new and difficult with only one arm. If he had two good arms, he'd run the whole river, even Rattan's Rapid, with its boulders and flying breakers. "Maybe I will anyway," he said aloud.

Though every movement hurt his bad arm, he kept on experimenting with ways of paddling one-armed. He stood up and sculled, he tried to row; neither was any good. At last he tied the paddle top to his upper arm with a bandanna and dipped along so, the paddle a rigid extension of his arm. The struggle to tie that one agonizing square knot left him cold with sweat and weak with pain. But he saw this was his best bet for the rapids. Kneeling in the bottom, he could paddle on either side and guide her somewhat.

By noon he was above Clifty Island, where, pinched between rock walls, the river rose in a great roaring surge. He walked along the cliffs and looked down. From island and rock wall the flying water leapt out in two curls of angry foam to meet at the point of a V; and streaking out from that pointed V was a mad, white, boiling roadway perhaps forty feet wide, raised by the enormous pressure a yard above the surrounding level. If a fellow could hit that V right nose-on, now—

While Jan watched, fascinated by the timeless, unwavering power of the white jet spurting from its funnel-mouth of rock, two ice pans converged from either wall, met at the apex, and crashed to pieces with a report like an explosion. He fingered his whiskers. That was something else to think about.

He walked rapidly back to the canoe, wedged the paddle top tight under the shoulder binding, and shoved off before he should have time to think about it. Drifting faster down the narrowing chasm, he shook his paddle in the air and shouted out, "Flipper, here we go." He stood up and scanned the banks of ice, knelt, and backed water furiously, first one side then the other. His backing did little to check the canoe's drop down the chute, but it slowed him sufficiently to allow a dirty ice block to career on before him. The white V-sides were lifting their curls beside him now, higher than his head, and he was deep in a gorge of sliding water within a gorge of rock.

A plunge, and he was into it, blinded by spume. She put her bow under, lifted up, and skittered down the hard, raised flume with water drumming on her as though from a gigantic fire hose. She was half-full, and the shore was a long way off, and the river was quiet again. Cautiously he worked toward a fair-sized pan that had come through intact. On the pan he threw his dripping gear, bailed the canoe with his teakettle, and hauled her up to turn her over. He stamped about on the floating ice, drenched to the skin, wringing water from his mitten with his teeth, the tied paddle trailing from his shoulder like some curious, misshapen limb.

A sound from downstream made him look up. Wild as a maniac, he threw his gear aboard, shoved off, and dug for the shore. Not a quarter of a mile below, a grinding ice wall stretched all across the river, barring the way. Here was the black river, there the gleaming whiteness of an ice bridge miles long.

That night he got to Hiram Meisher's cabin at Sidling Banks, beside a brawling tributary stream. The ice bridge was five miles long, and he had hauled his canoe across it on the toboggan. His snow glasses were lost, and the glare hurt his eyes. He decided that if he went snowblind, he'd shoot himself.

As he staggered into the cabin at dusk, he could not help wishing that Hiram were there with a candle lit and a fire going. Hi would have cooked for him and chopped wood and paddled him home, jolly, happy-go-lucky, glad of the chance to help, singing in the evening by the firelight to cheer him up.

Jan McKenzie, lone wolf, who traveled the river by himself, who fought his way up the rapids each fall alone, and home alone, who traveled farther and faster than anybody else and had no time for singing and yarns, felt lost and helpless for the first time in his weather-beaten career.

Well, by god, Jan McKenzie would manage for himself, same as he always had. He lit a fire in the home-made stove and put on the teakettle. But he was mighty glad of the dry wood in the corner, and he didn't chop any more to replace it.

Daylight came late. When Jan pushed off into the river again, it was snowing, a wet, miserable, clinging snow that hid the hills and made the day a dreary, age-long bleakness. A figure sheathed in white, in a whitened canoe, Jan paddled, paddled till his right arm knotted with cramps and ached as much as his left. The high hills above the river were hidden in the slow, silent snow, and even the sky was a dirty white, spilling out whiteness that enveloped everything but the black indelible river.

His left forearm was swollen nearly double normal size, and he began to think if he didn't get home soon he wouldn't make it at all. He ground his teeth and said to himself he was glad there was no one on the river to help him, especially Samson—Samson with his careful ways; Samson measuring the last of his sugar, pinch by pinch, into a teacup; Samson putting up a tent for a one-night camp as if he was setting about to build a church or found a city. If Samson had come swinging round the bend this very minute and offered help, Jan would have told him to clear out or get a clout on the head with a gun butt.

The little rapid known as McDonald's, after a Northern Trading Company Scotchman drowned there, wasn't bad, and Jan managed it handily, scooping the canoe now to the left, now to the right. At the Ruff by its lower end, where the current was said to surge up from a subterranean cliff sixty feet deep, he shipped a little water, but not much. Below there the river took a dip down three rapids through the last of the high hills. The first was Rattan's. Standing on a slippery boulder above it, peering through the snow, he saw it was impossible. The river split here into four wide channels below low, willowy islands, and every one of the channels was shallow and strewn with boulders over which spray shot fifteen and twenty feet into the air. With two good arms to drive the canoe faster than the current and so have some control, he could twist down through the tortuous channel, sweeping far to the right, then crossing to shoot through a deep break in the reef on the left bank. Often he had done it before. But with no power, drifting at the mercy of the current, he could never thread the hissing rocks.

To the waist in rushing water, he waded her down along the rocky western shore, guiding her through narrow runnels between boulders, pulling, pushing, slipping. He stepped into a hole and was swept from his feet, floated a few yards, and gained the shore again still gripping the canoe. He dragged her over a gravel bar around whose point the tide swept with a force he never could have stayed.

He was almost past the quick water, thinking how he'd let 'er rip down through the next two deep rapids as best he could, and the devil with it, when trouble came. He had reached a little cliffy place, below which lay another bad point. He was creeping along the rock ledges, letting the canoe drift at the end of the line. The other end was tied round his waist, a coil of it looped over his arm, and he took the strain with his teeth. His fingers lost their hold on the icy rock, he slipped to the shelf below, tottered, and pitched into the water. The coil of line wriggled from his arm as the canoe drifted faster toward the point. He floundered ashore by some rocks below the cliff and frenziedly hauled in slack. The canoe bobbed round the point and darted away in the full force of the tide's grip. He braced himself for the shock that was coming. With a singing snap the line yanked him five feet through the air, slammed him down on the stones with a sickening jar, and broke. He ran, screaming with pain, after the frayed end of rotten Manila that was wriggling in hops and twists across the point. He slipped on the ice of a crooked boulder and fell again. The line wriggled out of sight. Tears of rage were streaming down his cheeks, and his good fist was pounding, pounding the unfeeling rock.

Creeping over the crest of the point, he watched the canoe spin through a gap, swing broadside into a jagged rock, break slowly in half and disappear under the foam. She was gone now, with his ax, his tent, kettle, food, blanket, everything but the knife in his pocket and a few matches he had tucked in his hair for just such a last-ditch time as this. There was a meager satisfaction in remembering that all of his furs were safely cached back at his camp. Next year he would bring them out, maybe. . . .

Wearily he turned his back on the roaring river and climbed the mountainside through the thick trees. The snow was rotten with the warmth, and at every step he sank to the thigh and often to the waist. But he kept going, crawling sometimes on his knees and his one hand. Only ten miles down the river at the end of the last rapid was Peter Goudie's cabin. If he could get there along the hilltops, surely there'd be a canoe.

The snow stopped falling, and the sky cleared. Pulling himself up by the trees, crawling, falling, he gained the barren summit at sunset. He had been all afternoon making two miles. The snow was not so deep up there, blown off by the wind, and it was harder and bore him up better. Way off in the clear, cold west, scarlet clouds were gilding the ridges, turning the snow at his feet to gold and orange. The wet snow commenced to harden with frost, and from the deep valley of the river, mist slowly rose again. It was many years since he had felt so poignantly the vastness of the darkening wilderness around him. Evenings long ago his mother used to sit in the window of their house at sunset-time like this, looking across the ice, thinking of Pa. The sky was colored, and the far ridges melted as they did now, one beyond the other, into the sky and the night. And then she lit the lamp and got supper for Samson and Jan and herself in the yellow light in the warm, low house.

Wavering along the skyline, he made another mile. Then he descended to the trees and fell exhausted. Wet and shivering, hungry, weak with fever, he prowled around the trees in the dusk, looking for wood. This would be his worst night, he figured. Either he'd get to Peter's tomorrow night or he'd be done out.

The trees were small way up here, and some of them were dead. He built his fire of sticks against a cliff and made himself a bed of boughs before it. Dragging in all the dead trees he could, he burned them in half and piled them higher. At midnight he had to go out and look for more. A half-moon was sailing, white and cold in the night-blue sky, silvering the river mist, drawing purple dwarfed shadows under the trees. He looked up at the brightness of its serene, merciless face and knew it did not care whether his canoe was gone or his arm broken or whether he caved in and died, or lived. But he did not hate it; he had lived in the wilderness too long for that. He tore a strip from the bottom of his coat and bound his splints tighter, hoping to ease the pain that every movement brought. He only wished that he might ride across the sky as effortlessly as the sharp-edged moon.

Way down in the bottom of the valley, in the stillness of the night, he could hear the rapids roaring. Owls were hooting, answering each other miles and miles away on the mountainsides. He fell asleep, and steam rose from his back, and the front of his shirt stiffened with frost. The embers fell, and the purple tree-shadows moved across him.

Late the next night, by a clearing at whose edge the river gurgled coldly in and out among the stones, Jan stumbled off the mountainside, parted the ice-encrusted trees, and fell face foremost in the snow. He lay ten feet from a black and silent cabin, a speck beneath the mountain's looming bulk. Icicles hanging from the eaves shone dully in the weak moonlight.

Lifting up his head he called, "Peter, hello. Peter, Peter! Bound for home. Hello." His head fell into the snow. He commenced to laugh, an eerie, loathsome sound that started the echoes calling across the water in the luminous fog.

Then he humped up onto his knees and crawled. It took him five minutes to cover the ten feet to the door. He crept in, and the stove creaked, a light gleamed. Later he staggered out and filled a tea-kettle with snow.

The candle burned down, and the cabin was dark again; the fire burned out, and the kettle boiled dry. But Jan slept on.

It was noon when he woke and ransacked the cabin for food. Of beans and rice and pork he made soup. Of the flour he baked twenty bread cakes. For firewood he battered to pieces a three-legged stool, a grub box, and part of the bunk.

It was night, and calm, and he was drifting on the river again in the less leaky of Peter's two canoes. He lay in the bottom, rolled in a fur robe of Peter's, waking, sleeping, dreaming of the softness of a goose-down feather bed at home. It would be sealing time down there, and they'd have the motorboats all caulked and painted, and be launching them and chugging out to Jackfish Shoal to set the nets. There'd be ducks and geese by the thousands round the bay shore, and every house would be living on roast goose and fat black duck.

All next day he paddled and drifted down the widening river, its shores growing lower mile by mile. This was a new land, the land of home, and he should have been glad, but he kept falling asleep every little while. His arm had a dead numbness, and great drops of cold sweat were continually dropping off his forehead.

Night came and it was still calm. He must have fallen asleep again, for immediately it was sunrise, and the canoe was rocking violently. The breeze was blowing him ashore on a sandy beach where small waves broke. He stood on the sand, swaying in the rising wind, his long hair streaming out from under his cap, and he saw the bay, actually the bay and the whitecaps dancing on it a mile below him. He was home, home, almost.

He had only to walk a hundred feet down along the beach and climb a pinnacle of shore ice to see, two miles across the heaving river-mouth, the white dot that was the mission hospital, the green roofs of the trading post.

He tried to cross, but the wind kept pushing him back into the breakers. He had to run ashore again, and nearly swamped doing it.

Oh, curse the wind! Was he going to die here, looking at the village? He'd build a big fire in the night, he'd drag together a big pile of driftwood so they'd know it wasn't just duck hunters or Indians.

Even as he thought about it he laid his crippled arm down in the sand and crumpled up asleep beside it. In the night he built a small fire, but he wasn't strong enough to collect much driftwood, and the high wind soon burned it out. It was very cold, crouched on the lee of the overturned canoe. His arm began to throb clear to the shoulder and his fingers burned as though they were afire. Listening to the savage roar of surf, it seemed to him that this windy bayland with its stinging salt breath and wild desolate beaches was even less friendly than the river and the woods where he had lived so long.

At daylight the wind had dropped some. The sky looked unsettled and gusty, but Jan was unwilling to stay another hour on that freezing beach. This minute, now, before he fell asleep again, he'd have another try. He launched her out and rocked once more among the whitecaps. The bow lifted up and slapped down, checking him; a few seas slopped in, but he was making progress. If only someone would see him. He'd have been grateful to anyone, even to Samson, so he could rest and rest and sleep. But in the trough he was invisible, and on the crest he knew he looked little different from the drifting trees and dirty ice pans.

Black spots the size of a shotgun muzzle kept whizzing in front of his face, maddening as flies. In midstream, a mile from either shore, the wind veered and blew downriver, swinging his prow baywards. He knelt up closer to the bow and slopped along the left side, the wrong side, with all the strength of his failing body. But with the river's current and the stiffening wind pushing him out toward the wide gray bay he had no more chance than a stick of driftwood. The black dots whizzed faster with his desperate exertion, and he got so dizzy he was afraid he'd swamp himself, rolling so, broad-side-on. He fell into the bottom, sobbing like a child.

All this fighting down the river, only to go past. "I overdone it, little, seems like it," he muttered. If only he hadn't gone to sleep and down the wrong side, if only he'd crossed way up above where the river was narrower, and hugged that bank.

The waves splashed in on him, and he reached for Peter's kettle and bailed, almost without thinking about it. He was sliding out into the bay, past the village and the last sandpits, and what the use of bailing was he didn't know. He lifted his chin onto the gunnel and stared at the town. A nice place, with its row of houses, and the white sand beach and the boats anchored in the cove. He could see a thin white line that was the wood-path up the greenwoods hill behind the town. Smoke was streaming from a dozen stovepipes, and a flag was whipping from the trading-post pole. Feebly he waved his cap on the end of the paddle. And the wind blew his cap away. The canoe swung, and his eyes took in the vast emptiness of the lead-colored bay, twenty miles wide, a hundred miles to the sea. A fine chance he'd have out there in a canoe. If he had a hand to bail and a hand to steer, he might have tried sheering off with a rag of sail to that distant bluish shore in the east. He and Samson used to salmon-fish way over there by a creek-mouth, long ago when they were boys. But it was a lonely place. He could die here as well as there.

Then his dim eyes blazed. Dead leeward, like bent black reeds, were the weighted poles that marked the sealing buoys. He splashed out his flipper and whipped her up into the wind. Drifting fast like this, if he ever went by he'd never get back.

That afternoon the sealers found him out on the bay, rolling to and fro in the bottom of a canoe that was tied with triple knots to a seal-net buoy. As they shut off the motorboat and slid up close, they thought they were dreaming. "It's my old brown canoe, I swear," Peter Goudie said.

Four men in streaming oilskins, they peered over the gunnel, their quick eyes taking in the story of the sling, the paddle still bound to the shoulder, the bailer-kettle. One, as though it were his right, lifted the emaciated remains into the boat.

"Is he dead, Sam?" asked another.

"No," Samson answered, laying the body in the bottom on a tarpaulin. "He's breathin'."

Jan opened his eyes. "Breathin'?" he said. "I s'pose. Samson, you tell Peter I tore the innards right out of his cabin, but I'll pay 'm . . . double. I slept a night at your place . . . but I didn't . . . take . . . nothin'."

The men glared at Samson. "It serves you right, Sam," said one. "He never stole your flour, and you've always known it."

Jan seemed to hear. He shook his head like a dog coming out of water and he hove himself onto one elbow. "Sam," he said in a low voice, "I lied. I ate up all your rice 'n' pork . . . 'n' I couldn't've made it without."

Samson knew he lied, because there wasn't any rice or pork up there. But he said, "That's right, Jan. I'm glad, Jan," and he wrapped the canvas closer round his brother.

WITHOUT WORDS

JAN McKENZIE came over a knoll and stopped, head back, his rifle in one mitten, his ax in the other. Below him spread the river, ice-locked between the hills. A mile across, the birch bluffs were turning blue in the twilight.

He was not given to poetic fancies, for that is not the way of a Scotch-Eskimo trapper alone in the middle of Labrador. Nevertheless, it touched him always, coming out to the river after days and nights in the spruces to the east, following brooks and nameless chains of lakes that didn't lead anywhere, plowing through willow tangles and up and down wooded hills. It gave him a feeling of spaciousness, like stepping out of doors to see the broad river again, sweeping out of sight between the hills. The river was a known thread that joined him to the nearest trapper fifty miles downstream. The river was the road to home and to his wife, Luce.

It was nine weeks now since the day in September when his canoe and the others from Turner's Harbor had swung off from the wharf and begun the upstream battle. The crowd had waved, and the double-barreled shotguns split the air in the old-time farewell, *Boomboom* . . . and a pause to load . . . *Boom*, saying, "Good-bye . . . Luck." Then the trappers floating on the river in their loaded canoes raised their guns and fired one answering shot, "Luck." They picked up their paddles and disappeared around the point, to be gone five months. Sometimes, even when they'd passed around the point and the town was lost, they could still hear the guns, *Boomboom . . . Boom,* like a last calling. It gave a fellow something to remember way off here where you didn't hear anything much except your own voice.

It would be pretty near three months yet before he'd be home with his fur to Luce, he was thinking as he scrambled down the bank and legged it along the ice for "the house." This cabin had a window, and a door with hinges, a good tight roof of birch bark, and, within, such luxuries as a sleeping bag, which his tiny log-tilts back in the woods had not.

It was nearly dark when he got there, but not too dark to see in the cove the print of strange snowshoes. And by the point where the current flowed fast and the ice was thin, somebody had been chopping a water hole.

"Hello," he called to the cabin.

From the ridge came a silvery, mocking "hello," and faintly, seconds later, a distant hello across the river, the echo of the echo. Jan crossed the cove bent double, studying the tracks. There were three of them, a big pair of snowshoes and two smaller pairs. The smaller snowshoes had been dragging in a stick of firewood from alongshore—the women.

Jan threw off his bag and hurried into the cabin. Nobody made snowshoes of that pattern but Mathieu Susaka-shish, the Seven Islands Indian. Nobody but Mathieu knew this cabin was here. He and his wife and daughter had come last year and begged a little tea and sugar. Now they had been here again with their Indian idea that food belongs to anybody who is hungry. The devils! Where three fifty-pound bags of flour had been hanging, only two hung now. They had dripped candle grease onto his bunk and left his big meat kettle unwashed. He dove under the bunk and pulled out his food boxes. They'd made off with some of his split peas and a few of his beans, a handful of candles too. They had sliced a big chunk of salt pork neatly down the middle.

In a frenzy of rage he ripped open his fur-bag. Every skin was there, and in addition, a black and shining otter skin lay crosswise on his bundles of mink and marten, fox and ermine. He held it up and blew the hair and felt its thickness and its length, stroking its blue-black luster. It was a prize, it would bring sixty dollars, perhaps. But the sight of it made him angrier than before.

"So!" he muttered. "Mathieu thinks one miserable skin of fur pays me for my grub, eh?" He lit a candle, and his hand was trembling with rage. From now on he'd be half-hungry all the time, and hunting meat when he ought to be tending the trap line. He thought of his wife, and the blankets, and the windows, and the boat and nets and the new stove they needed at home. This was his whole year's earnings, these five months in the bush. And Mathieu thought he could steal the grub that made it possible, did he? He thought he could come every year and fit himself out, likely.

Jan took his rifle and emptied the magazine. It was only one bag of flour—but still, there were men way off here in the country who'd died for lack of a cupful, yes, a spoonful. Slowly he reloaded with the soft-nosed cartridges he kept for caribou. Would he tell Luce, would he ever be able to forget that somewhere back in the ridges, by some secret little lake that no one knew, he had shot three Indians and stuffed them through the ice? Didn't the Bible say, an eye for an eye and a tooth for a tooth?

There was bannock bread to bake and fur to be skinned. It was nearly midnight when he stoked up the stove and rolled in on the bunk for the last good sleep he expected to know for a while. At five o'clock in the starlight he was out on the river shore with a candle lantern made out of a baking-powder can, examining tracks. The polished, shallow trench which their two toboggans had left was so plain that a child could have followed it. Mathieu was ahead, taking long steps, hurrying. The two women were behind, hauling their toboggan in double harness, tandem-fashion. One of them fell and left the print of her knee going down the bank. Jan smiled as though he had seen it and heard her mutter.

He followed their track across the river to the top of a draw between two bare hills. There in the sunrise he turned and looked back at the ice sparkling with frost in the soft golden light, spotted with long blue shadows of the hills. As he plunged downhill into the thick country to the north he had an ominous feeling that he was leaving something. Maybe Mathieu would ambush him; it would be an easy thing to do on a track like this. Would Mathieu guess that he was being chased?

Jan studied the track, unconsciously noting every detail. Here in this book of the snow he might perhaps read Mathieu's thoughts, even a warning of an ambush. Indians were smart in the woods. Did he really think he could out-track an Indian hunter?

"By the Lord Harry, I can have a try," he whispered to himself.

Two mornings ago it was, that they passed through here under the firs, across that little brook. Two days was not much start for them. They had sleds and he had none. Mathieu had to break trail, while he had their hard frozen track to walk on. They had all their winter gear, their blankets and kettles, their tin stove and tent, traps, trout nets probably. He had nothing but the gamebag on his back, nine cakes of bread, tea and sugar, rifle and ax, a single blanket. The chances were he could travel twice as fast as they.

He passed their first fire, where they had stopped to boil tea and had thrown the tea leaves on the embers. The tea leaves were frozen stiff.

All day he swung on, parting the boughs where the spruces were thick, slipping through them as effortlessly as a weasel, trotting down all the hills with a tireless shuffle, trotting again where the way was level and open. Once he stopped for ten minutes to sit on a log and munch dry bread, light his pipe, and swing on. It was frosty, and the edges of his fur cap grew white with his breathing.

Before sunset he had long passed their first night's camp. Through the semi-darkness of early twilight he pressed on, following the hardness of their track more by touch than by sight. In the starlight he made his fire and boiled tea in a ravine by a brook. Here and there a tree snapped with the frost. The brook murmured under the ice. On the western hill a horn owl was hooting.

Every hour he woke with the cold, threw on more wood, turned over and slept again. Around three o'clock he woke and could not sleep again. He sat hunched in the blanket, looking into the fire thinking what a fool he was. He should be on the trap line, not here. He had not come up the river so far away to waste time chasing Indians around the hills. Already he was hungry and wished he had brought more food. It was too bad he couldn't just shoot Mathieu, but it would be no use to leave the women to wander around and starve. At the thought of actually squeezing the trigger and seeing them drop, he shuddered.

By half past four he had boiled his tea and eaten, and was picking his way along the track again. He should have rested another hour, he knew; it was so slow in the darkness. But he could not rest, though he was tired. He wanted to get it over with. Probably they would not bleed much; it was so cold.

The Indians were still heading northwest. Likely they were bound for the hundred-mile lake, Panchikamats, not far from the headwaters of streams that flowed into Hudson's Bay. Mathieu would feel safe there. And he would be, too. It was much farther than Jan could track him, with only three days' grub in the bag.

In the morning he passed their second night's camp. By noontime he had come to the edge of a big, oval marsh that was about six miles wide at its narrowest. On its barren floor there were occasional clumps of dead sticks, juniper and fir, no higher than a man's head, the firs rotten and falling, the junipers gaunt and wind-carved. Compared to its bleak, dead savagery the greenwoods borders seemed sociable and friendly and snug. As the merciless northwest wind had stunted and killed the trees, so it could shrivel and kill a man if it caught him out there in a blizzard.

The trail was dim and wind-scoured. A mile out and there was nothing but the dully shining spots the sleds had polished; two miles out and Mathieu was veering off to the east, deviating now from his northwest course.

The marks petered out entirely, heading, at the last, straight east. If Mathieu were really heading northwest, the blue notch at the marsh's far end was the natural way for him. Then why, in the middle of the marsh, did he swing off for the steep ridges to the east?

Jan trotted about in a circle, slapping his mittens together and pounding the toes that were aching in his moccasins. The drifting snow slid by like sand, rising in little eddies as the wind rose.

He stopped and stood with his back to the wind, leaning against it. Mathieu, he figured, wanted to go through the blue notch, but it was too plain. He knew his track could be picked up there first thing. So he cut off in the middle of the marsh, thinking there'd be no mark of it left. Mathieu had just made a little circle-round, and was now right on down the valley. With the women hauling sleds, they couldn't get along in those hills. They'd have to strike the valley.

Jan picked up his gamebag and trotted off toward the now-invisible notch. Lord Harry, he was hungry. In the wind he felt like singing; the wind drowned sound, sang a song of its own, saved a man from feeling that the miles of quiet woods were listening. He roared in a strong baritone:

> Oh we seen the strangest sights of far-off lands,
> And we conquered stormy winds and stinging foam,
> But the be-e-est is to see the chee-eery lights of ho-o-ome.

The drift had obscured the shores now, and he was as though alone in the middle of a white sea, snow above, below, and on all sides. But he did not think of it. The wind was compass enough for him and had been since boyhood.

He clasped his gun and ax in the crook of one elbow, put his curled mitts up around his mouth, and imitated a mouth organ, hunching up his shoulders and swinging his body, dancing on his snowshoes in the gale.

At dusk, miles beyond the blue notch, he picked up the Indians' track again. He glowed with the warmth of a hunter's pride. They'd never get away now; they were doomed, unless it snowed.

A mile farther on they had camped, and there he camped too. There was still a faint warmth in the depths of their ashes. But the sight of a bundle lashed in the low branches of a spruce made him pause. It was a hairy caribou skin, a big trout net, and a heavyish iron Dutch oven. So, they were lightening loads, were they? They knew they were being tracked then. How did they know?

Jan sat on the fir brush of their tent site and thought about it. They didn't know, they couldn't know. Mathieu was just playing safe, that was all, announcing, if he should be followed, that he was still a-drivin' 'er for all he was worth, bluffing a pursuer, trying to say, "I know I am being followed"—just in case he should be followed. Mathieu would go on for a week, get his women set in a good camp, then circle back, hunting as he came, and pick up his stuff again.

That's what you think, Mathieu.

That night he ate another half a bannock, only half when he could so easily have eaten three whole ones. What a fool he was to have traveled so light. If, by some mischance, he didn't catch them now, he'd be stranded off here with nothing to eat.

Rolled in his blanket and their caribou robe, he had the best sleep yet. It was risky. He had his gun beside him. For why couldn't Mathieu come back tonight as well as in a week? All about was the ring of darkness; here was the firelight. What a perfect mark to shoot at. Yes, but Mathieu wouldn't shoot him. Why, Mathieu's father used to camp on the shore at Turner's Harbor in the summertime years ago. Mathieu's cousin used to wrestle with Jan by the hour, and Mathieu himself had been in the foot races they ran on the beach by the blue, cool bay long ago.

He sat and poked at the fire. Mathieu wouldn't shoot you, he was thinking, but you'd shoot Mathieu. Mathieu would steal his grub, but he wouldn't steal Mathieu's grub. Head in hands, he rocked to and fro, bewildered and hating this mental tangle. Oh, if Mathieu only hadn't come along at all; if only Mathieu hadn't taken a whole bag of flour, he would be so glad for Mathieu.

He settled it this way: if Mathieu wants to come along and shoot me tonight, let him, that's good luck for Mathieu; but if Mathieu doesn't, maybe Mathieu will get shot himself tomorrow night.

The stars paled and the east grayed the same as on other mornings. Jan did not set out until there was a little light. It would be so easy for Mathieu to wait hidden by the track.

He walked with his cap on the side, exposing one ear, and when that ear began to freeze he tilted his cap and uncovered the other. Every mile he stopped and listened, mouth open, holding his breath. Late in the forenoon as he stood examining a small valley thick with willows and boulders, he was conscious from the corner of his eye that a tuft of snow was slipping down the face of a gray boulder off to the left. Was somebody behind there? He turned and ran, dodging through the trees. Skirting the end of the willows, he stealthily approached the trail farther on. No, no one had been there. It must have been a willow twig brushing the rock in the breeze. Here were the three prints, just the three prints, Mathieu's almost indistinguishable under the women's and the sleds'. The women had given up hauling tandem. They took turns single, and when they changed places Mathieu didn't wait for them. They had to run a little to catch up, poor things. Luce could never have hauled like that.

As he tramped, he got to thinking of the otter skin Mathieu had left. It was funny the way Indian hunters would take food. They'd been hunters for so many ages they thought a bag of flour, like a caribou, was anybody's who needed it. But they wouldn't steal fur. Indians! They were like a necessary evil, they were like children. It would be better if they *did* steal fur and left the grub alone. They could pack grub as well as anybody, but they let the trappers wear themselves to skin and bone struggling up the river in a canoe loaded to the gunwales, risking their lives for it in the white rapids, lugging their loads up the Great Bank, a mile long and steeper than the bridge of Satan's own nose, breaking their backs for it across twelve miles of swamps and brooks and slippery rocks on the Grand Portage, where the tumplines pulled their hair out by the roots and they carried till their eyes turned black and their trembling knees sagged under them. And then—then the Indians came along and helped themselves as though flour were worth no more up here than down on the bay shore.

They won't help themselves to my grub, Jan thought grimly. Some day I'll come back to the house maybe and find it cleaned right out. And what about me, living on jay's legs and moss till I fall in the snow and die?

The sky was growing deeper gray, darkness coming early. The air was chill with a suspicion of dampness. Come a big batch of snow to cover their track and make the walking back heavy, he'd be in a fine fix with no food. He smelled the wind, and it smelled like snow. Before dark it began to fall, and at dark he still had not caught them. Must be getting weak, he thought ruefully. He'd set some rabbit snares tonight. Or maybe he'd get a partridge. And maybe he wouldn't.

He stood on the shore of a little lake and leaned against a tree, uncertain. With the new snow and the dark, there was only the barest sign of the track now. By morning it would be gone. What was the sharp smell?

He threw back his head and sniffed. Wood smoke! He had caught them. Let the snow pelt down, let it snow six feet in the night; he had caught them and they couldn't get away.

Strange, though, that they should camp before the snow got thick. An hour more and they would have been safe. Well, Mathieu had made his last mistake this time.

Over a knoll in a thick clump of firs Jan built a small fire to boil a kettle. He was ravenous, and weary to the bone. They were camped, they would keep till he got ready for them. And they couldn't smell his smoke with the wind this way.

He ate the last of his bannock, drank four cups of tea, and smoked his pipe to the last dregs. Then he left his bag and ax, took his rifle, and stole out across the dark lake. It was black as ink, and the new snow was like cotton wool to muffle his steps. Just back from the far shore he saw their dome-shaped *meetchwop* glimmering. They were burning a candle in there, one of his own probably.

He crept up closer on his belly, foot by foot. The two sleds were stuck up against a tree; there was the chopping block, the ax, the chips. Snowshoes were hanging from a limb, the two small pairs.

The women inside were baking bread. He could hear the frying pan scrape on the tin stove. They were talking in their soft, musical voices, more like a brook under the ice than like human talk. But he could not bring himself to walk into the tent and shoot them in cold blood. Better get Mathieu first. But where were the big snow-shoes—where was Mathieu? Behind that black tree there with his rifle cocked?

He lay silent, scarcely breathing, ears stretched for the slightest sound. There were only the wind and the falling snow and the women's voices and the scraping pan.

Fifteen minutes, a half-hour, he lay thus. He was freezing, he couldn't lie there all night. Inch by inch, he crawled away. Silent as a shadow, he went back across the lake. There was danger every-where now, every time he moved a muscle. He could feel it all around him, feel a prickling in his scalp and a supernatural cer-tainty that as he was stalking Mathieu, Mathieu was stalking him. Cautiously, with long waits, he approached his camp. The fire was out. His fingers touched the gamebag and drew back. Something was there, something that shouldn't be! *Something was wrong.* Chills went up and down his spine. He whirled toward a deeper patch of shadow, knowing with the certainty of panic that gunfire would belch from that shadow and blind him. His eyes roamed round in his head in the darkness and he waited, turned to stone.

There was no sound. Nothing but the soft hiss of snowflakes drifting down.

Then he smelled it. Bread, new-baked bread, sweet as life to his nostrils. He drew off his mitten and touched the gamebag again. His fingers counted them—seven crusty bannock cakes, still warm.

"Mathieu," he whispered to the engulfing darkness. There was no answer. He struck a match and looked at the cakes. He bit one, and shook his head, ashamed. All his muscles sagged as he slumped into the snow and took a deep, deep breath—the first, it seemed, in many days.

Everything was different now. Noisily he crashed down a big tree for his night's fire. He was sticking up a lean-to by the fireplace, he was chilled by the night's cold, not by the cold horror of that other unthinkable job. Lord, he'd rather Mathieu plugged him full of holes than to take a sight on Mathieu. It was like waking up from a nightmare. He had half a mind to go across the lake now and ask

Mathieu's woman to sew up the tear in his britches, and have a good sleep in the Indians' warm tent. How they would giggle and talk with their black eyes!

But he was too ashamed. Mathieu was a better man than he was, that was all—smarter in the woods and more forgiving. I wouldn't forgive Mathieu, he mused, for taking a bag of flour, but he forgives me for trying to kill him. All the time the snow's coming down and he only had to go on a little piece farther tonight to lose me. He knows that, but he takes a chance and sneaks back to feed me, me that's chasing him to kill him. Mathieu don't want I should starve going back to the river. Mathieu—he don't want us to part unfriendly.

Lord, it beat all. If ever he told this to Luce she'd say he was the head liar out of all the liars on the whole river.

He finished one of the fragrant, tender bread cakes and lay down with his back to the fire. It was a long time since he'd felt so happy. Wonderful strange too, how much he and Mathieu had said to each other without words, way off here, never meeting, eating each other's grub.

Toward morning the snow stopped. Just after sunrise the Indian family broke camp and climbed the hill up from the shore. Jan, watching from the opposite hill across the lake, saw them silhouetted, three dark figures on the bare ridge. He pointed his gun at a tree top and let go greeting. *Boomboom . . . Boom.* He saw the two women, startled, duck behind their sled.

But Mathieu stood erect against the brightening sky. He raised his rifle and fired one answering shot.

So they stood for a moment, on opposite hills, with upraised hands. *Good-bye. Luck.*

MINA PADDON AND THE
WINTER OF THE FLU

HIS STORY CONCERNS MINA PADDON, who lived through the 1918–19 winter of the flu and has described that time for me. Born Mina Gilchrist, in Nova Scotia, she grew up there and went to Boston to train at Massachusetts General Hospital. In 1911, when she had acquired her registered nurse's certificate, she thought she would try nursing for a year at the Grenfell Mission Hospital in St. Anthony, northern Newfoundland. She took the steamer to St. John's, Newfoundland. A man there told her that at the Mission hospital in St. Anthony they had thirty patients and only one nurse. The narrow-gauge train north through the outports to Twillingate broke down and took all day to get rolling again. From Twillingate to St. Anthony travelers continued north by motorboat, skirting the rocky islands, crossing wide stretches of open ocean. Mina was very seasick, and very annoyed even in her misery.

Coming into the calmer reaches of St. Anthony harbor, she gathered herself together, and it was well she did. Dr. John Little was waiting for her on the wharf. "How do you do, Miss Gilchrist," he said. "I'm glad to meet you."

She smiled and thought of the thirty patients. "Yes," she said, "I suppose you are."

When they got to know her, they joked about that. It was typical—very reticent one moment, very outspoken the next. They found she was a good nurse with special training in anesthetics, and a terrific worker.

More than twenty thousand fishermen harvested cod along the Labrador in those summers. Mina was sent across the Straits to Battle Harbour in the spring to open up the branch hospital there with another nurse, the one and only Miss Carlson, a flaxen-haired Norwegian who became almost like a sister. One of Miss Carlson's frequent feats was to dive off an icepan in the harbor and swim about very happily in the paralyzing water, blowing like a porpoise and laughing at everybody who begged her to come out.

Mina went to Indian Harbour, most northerly medical station. There she and the young English doctor, Harry Paddon, fell in love. A year later they were married, and in the autumn when the coast closed down and the schooners all sailed south, the newlyweds made the first of many epic voyages in the Mission ketch *Yale* up Hamilton Inlet to the inland settlements of Labrador. The first winter was in an abandoned lumber camp at Mud Lake; water froze on the dinner table one evening. They built the first hospital at North West River. It burned down, and they and the Mission struggled to raise money for another, for a school, for boarding cottages.

The poverty, beriberi, and tuberculosis of the lungs and bones were unbelievable along the Labrador in those days. The doctors and nurses and others fought on. During the short summers, *Yale* gathered up T.B. and other patients for North West River hospital and many more for St. Anthony. It was essential to reduce sources of tuberculosis infection. Later, the hospital vessel *Maraval* traveled tens of thousands of miles on the same job.

In that period the ill-governed Crown Colony of Newfoundland was able to do little for Labrador—except charge heavy customs duties on traps, guns, fishing gear, clothing, and most of the necessities of life. The Hudson's Bay Company gave low pay for furs and put a high price on supplies. Coastal fishermen, working in the finest codfishing ground in the world, suffered under the cruel old sharecropper system, whereby the summer's catch was mortgaged to fish merchants before it was caught. These conditions had much to do with the prevalent poverty in a land whose most favored areas produced fish, furs, berries, and game.

In winter Dr. Paddon made long dogteam journeys north to the Eskimo settlements of Hopedale and Nain, east to Cartwright, south to Battle Harbour. He became an enduring traveler on the winter trail. Mina tried not to worry when he was weeks overdue, when the leads in the ice opened and spring breakup came, and still the Mission twelve-dog team had not returned. She was the Doctor's Wife, and everyone looked to her for strength and advice and reassurance. She refused to take the glasses and peer down the bay for the black dots that moved—or didn't they? At such times the women of the village had a way of dropping in more frequently, for a cup of tea, for a chat. They didn't say, but they knew.

The doctor and his wife led many lives. In summer it was the barren, rocky coast, codfish, schooners, ocean. At sunset two dozen schooners often rounded up with shaking sails and let go in Indian Harbour. The kerosene lamps burned late at the hospital.

Winter was the inland, the forest, the rivers and lakes, a different people, all travel on the ice by snowshoe or dogteam. The Paddons early saw the economic opportunities offered Labradormen by North West River's favored site and conditions. "Eden of the North" they called it, half in jest at midwinter, half in earnest in the springtime when migrating ducks and geese crosshatched the blue water and white icepans with their millions. It was a unique place, the village at the head of the estuary, where half a dozen rivers entered, gateway to the wilderness. In winter the trapper men were gone up those rivers into the bush. At the onset of summer, the Montagnais Indians in their canoes, and a few Naskapi, came paddling down the streams from their wanderings in the thousands of miles of forests and lakes and barrens to the west. The hunting and the fishing, the caribou and the sealing, the berry-picking and the wood hauling each came according to its season. In winter two dogteam mails from the southern world arrived between November and June. Blizzards piled snow up to the windows, but there was also much sunshine. It was a different climate from that on the coast, literally and figuratively.

In the course of a full existence Mina produced four sons and brought them up. Her eldest son, Anthony, became a doctor who in World War II served aboard Canadian Navy corvettes and frigates four years during the Battle of the Atlantic. Subsequently he took his father's place at North West River and was still Chief Medical Officer for the Northern District in 1976. Later he became Lieutenant Governor of Newfoundland.

In a thousand emergencies Mina filled the gap and ran the hospital—not only the hospital but the clothing store, the handicraft projects, the school, and the station as a whole. At first it was her job. Later, as wife and mother, she just did it on the side whenever a short-handed staff needed help. She nursed all through the 1919 influenza epidemic that was the worst killer the coast had ever known. During the four years after her husband died (in 1939) there was no doctor. She held the place together during World War II. She served the Grenfell Mission all her life, but not so much the Mission as the people of Labrador. She loved them and they loved her. She retold their stories and rocked their children's children. She was like Sir Wilfred Grenfell—with whom she didn't always agree—in that she improved the gardens and the nutrition and she comforted the mothers and birthed the babies and assisted the surgeons and dentists primarily because she loved to, because it gave her strength and joy. Whenever friends in the U.S., Canada, or Britain expressed regret for her isolation amid the subarctic snows in that faraway place, she knew they didn't understand. "I have had a wonderful life," she used to say. When she was awarded the Order of the British Empire for her work in Labrador and asked to come to St. John's for presentation ceremonies, she sent her thanks and said, "Please mail it, as I am very busy here."

In 1967, at age 86, Mina died in her North West River home. The trapper, Indian, and Eskimo families for two hundred miles around lamented her passing. She had done something helpful and happy for almost every one of them. She was the grand old lady of Labrador, and there will never be anyone like her.

Several years before she died, she told me most of the following story.

Nineteen eighteen, the year World War I ended, and 1919 were the years of the flu. Nobody knows how many millions it killed throughout the world. It struck hammer blows on the Labrador coast, wiping out whole villages of people too weak even to help one another. During all that terrible winter Dr. Paddon was the only doctor on the Labrador coast.

The germ arrived aboard the last mail steamer of the 1918 summer, at the onset of winter. In Hamilton Inlet the specific agent of transmittal was a motorboat from Mud Lake that had gone ninety miles to Rigolet to meet the steamer for freight, as often happened. The skipper of the motorboat was laid low almost immediately after his return trip up the bay. The flu spread, and many

Mud Lakers died. Northward the infection traveled from the same coastal mailboat to Hopedale and Nain and beyond.

At Okak, north of Nain, not a man was left. All the surviving women and children of that 260-person village were later brought south on two komatiks. At Hebron also, a town formerly numbering 170, every breadwinner died. On one island nobody was left but a little girl who had gone quite wild. She had curled up with the dogs for warmth, and when rescuers came ashore in a boat they had to run her down to catch her. Hundreds of children were left without parents. A famous old woman in one of the coast settlements who was left sick and alone couldn't make a fire in the house for eleven days lest the frozen corpses thaw. When the water barrel froze, she chipped out pieces of ice and melted them in a small cup in her armpits, and thus somehow survived on icewater and half-frozen bread.

Practically everyone in North West River was down with it in November, Dr. Paddon among the first. But he was soon up again, tottering around thin and hollow-eyed. Miss Carlson, wonderful Miss Carlson, was nurse there that year. People in the village couldn't even make fires, and whole households were on the verge of freezing to death. All who were sick had severe nosebleeds. It was more like a plague than any epidemic the modern world has known (and bore small resemblance to what in later years became known as "flu"). This scourge was frequently called bubonic pneumonia. Very commonly, a strong man would within two days be gasping for breath, with a fever of 106, and on the third day be dead. This horrible member of The Four Horsemen killed more people throughout the world than all those who died in World War I. In Labrador, where most of the population is part-Eskimo, a race for whom even measles and whooping cough are often fatal, the pulmonary curse left an unbelievable trail of corpses.

Dr. Paddon and Miss Carlson went round the village making fires and feeding people. Mina did the cooking, principally huge kettles of soup. She couldn't help thinking of her own, and kept saying, "If only the boys don't get it." There was the big team of Mission sled dogs to feed, the corn meal to boil and the seal fat to mix, and this was only one of her jobs. There had been a big shipment of apples on the last boat, so she made baked apples by the hundreds and everybody loved them. There were the pigs and chickens to feed, and Mina had to do that. When she saw a little lantern come bobbing late at night, she knew it was Miss Carlson or Doctor, home from their rounds for a few hours sleep before starting out again. It was a time of Herculean labors, as so often happens in the north, when there is no leeway for anyone to falter, when the work grinds on until one wonders where the strength to continue comes from. But it does come and keeps coming.

And then the Paddon children fell sick, of course.

The village boats had been hauled up on shore for the winter and huge tepee-like stacks of firewood piled near the shore in readiness for sawing. To add to the troubles, an in-wind storm blew up the bay for days and days before freeze-up, raising the water far above ordinary marks, and floated away most of the precious boats and firewood. Nobody could be spared for the time being to go after them.

Miss Carlson was a tower of strength and never stopped working day or night, it seemed. She was always cheerful, always gay, her fortitude and strength never failing. She and Mina were the only people in North West River who didn't get the flu.

Thanks to all the efforts, only two people in the village died, and by and by the rest began to recover and emerge, weakly. It took months to get strong again. Even before they were well, the available men set off to find the boats, and salvaged most of them.

In Cartwright and Sandwich Bay things went very badly and nearly half the population died. Reverend Henry Gordon, Church of England minister and well-loved figure on all the coast, was there doing his best but he could not cope with it all—not even with the burials.

That was a terrible winter of starvation, one of those years when there seemed to be no partridges, no rabbits, no caribou, nothing. Ordinarily there was a good supply of meat for the hunting, but this was the down cycle, and where the game had gone to no one could imagine. People picking up from the debilitating flu, in danger of relapse, were starving.

Though North West River had a radio for the first time, with Jack Watts, man of many talents, there to work it, equipment was inadequate and communication scant.

Mina said, "About all we ever got was the price of wheat in Russia. We were so thrilled. Harry had paid the operator of the big government radio station at Battle Harbour to write out any important news for us and send it along by the winter dog team mails (two). But all the Battle Harbour man ever said was, 'Dog team leaving. No time. More later.' It was most unsatisfactory. We were wondering and wondering how the war was going, but we did not get word of the November 11 Armistice until January 28, 1919. Then all the men in the village stacked a huge pile of wood on the thick ice of the river shallows in front of the town and had a bonfire and celebration. I took the boys out to see it, though it was long past their bedtime. I wanted them to remember the end of the World War. I thought of all the millions dead, all the courage, all the sorrow. They didn't think of things like that, they were so young. Yet it remains one of their most vivid memories—the great fire, the war over. All their earliest memories seem to be linked with fires, usually campfires. This one made a great impression on them.

"Harry had to go away on his winter dogteam trip, down the bay and to Cartwright and the north coast. The round trip was about twelve hundred miles. Things were desperate that year, with the flu, the orphaned children, the lack of game, so many people starving.

"You know, every summer the Doctor sent around boxes of food and supplies by boat to homes at strategic settlements so that he could provide for himself and his dogs on the winter trip and not have to use other people's food. Each winter I think he gave away most of it. At any rate, the Doctor's box got to be a famous matter, especially for the children, wondering what was in it, wondering whether there were any of those little mince pies I used to bake. They were extra useful, I thought, because they didn't freeze on dog team journeys and could be eaten any time. I have met children from all over Labrador who told me years later how good those mince pies were, so I don't believe Harry ate very many of them.

"This bad year, it was amazing and touching how nobody would dip into the box. When he arrived at a home and found how short they were, Harry wished they had. He told them they should have helped themselves. But they didn't think it was right, and so they went on with their bread and tea and a little salt fish and not much of that.

"In those years the Newfoundland government used to send down a few itinerant schoolteachers, women or men. The women were usually better teachers. They stayed at one house or settlement for a few weeks or a month and then moved on somewhere else to give the children what they could of the three R's. There was a spunky young woman teaching that winter at Jerry Flowers' place in Flowers' Cove, near Rigolet, when the flu struck. They were all sick, all in bed scarcely able to move except for one tall, slender fellow with a white bandage wrapped around his face for a toothache. She lay there in her little board room with her fever and her weakness and, I suppose, her delirium. Most everybody was delirious. And—she told us—every morning this tall apparition with the white rag would look in on her and solemnly shout to the others, 'She ain't dead yet.' This went on every morning and made her so mad she later believed it contributed to her recovery.

"For years it was a joke with us, *She ain't dead yet*, and the expression cheered us in all sorts of trying situations.

"When Harry came along, this same teacher was at Double Mer and not getting much to eat. For Christmas dinner all they had was a few stewed redberries and some molasses. The Doctor's box was there, but nobody would open it. He told her she should have, she was so weak. Harry thought she'd have a relapse and die if something wasn't done, so he sent her up the bay to me and I built her up with good food and rest for a while. She was a courageous person, and we had lots of fun. When she was better, I sent her to Mulligans, to the Baikies. They have always been good hunters and wonderfully hard workers and live fairly well. She recovered there so that she could teach again.

"During his winter trip Harry and his dogdriver were sledging down the Backway toward Cartwright one gray, cold day. You can scarcely imagine how limitless the bay ice seems on a sunless day, with the snow crystals seeping past like sand and the mountains blue in the sky looking down at you. Far off they saw two black specks, men, swinging their arms, obviously hauling toboggans. There on the ice that winter afternoon he had a reunion with Murdock McLean and Robert Michelin, two of the finest trappers in the bay. They had gone to the war, served a long time in the trenches in France, and here they were, on the way home after two and a half years abroad. Robert lived up Grand River at Traverspine, and was the son of old Uncle Joe Michelin, who had some French and Indian progenitors. Murdock was one of blue-eyed

Malcolm McLean's twenty-three children—Malcolm, the Scottish patriarch who had bred himself a whole village at Kenemish, across the bay from North West River. Murdock's mother had been a full-blooded Eskimo, the first of his father's three wives.

"There was much news to exchange, of course. Robert had been wounded in the leg and had a slight limp. The Army surgeons had told him they weren't sure he could ever snowshoe and hunt again. When he and Murdock had been demobilized and sent back to Newfoundland, it was autumn, and they were informed it was too late to get back to Labrador; the last regular steamer trip across the Straits of Belle Isle was over and they would have to winter in New- foundland. I can imagine them looking at their informant intently, with their dark eyes wide open, not saying anything, those hunters. They got a small boat across to Battle Harbour somehow before the Straits froze over, and there they provided themselves with snow- shoes, made toboggans, and patched together other necessary gear. They came along the coast and around the seaward toe of the Mealy Mountains, a walk of about five hundred miles the way they went. They had not been over the route before, but as hunters and trappers they had spent half their lives in the bush, and such men have an uncanny way of never being lost. Harry couldn't think who they were at first, two dark figures way out on the ice.

"They told him they were glad to be back. His years in the trenches in France had not crushed Murdock. He was fond of English understatement and liked to outdo them at it. Murdock said, 'There's been times, Doctor, when I never thought to see you again.'

"In that year of poor hunting, rabbits were still unavailable. We couldn't remember such a year. In making up our yearly requisi- tion for supplies, we did not ask for much meat because we counted on considerable fresh supplies that would be brought in locally in exchange for clothing. But no fresh meat was to be had. Finally, one of the hunters up Grand Lake sent two partridges, one for me and one for the children. It was the first fresh meat we had seen all winter, and I was very touched by this gift that had come hand to hand, passed along from one trapper to another, for me, when they all needed it as much as I did, and more. The partridges had no sooner arrived than in came Reverend Gordon by dogteam from Cartwright. He looked ghastly and had had a terrible winter, with the flu, and the food so short, so I told Kitty Montague, who was cooking that year, to cook up one of the precious partridges for Gordon's supper and I'd save the other for the children.

"When open water arrived and the ducks and geese came in that spring, we were so glad we didn't know what to do."

That summer the dormitory and boarding school projects were started at Cartwright to take care of children whose mothers and fathers had died. Reverend Gordon subsequently devoted months to raising money for it, and Dr. Paddon wore himself out on the lecture platforms of the United States getting funds for the buildings. He raised a major portion of what was needed. Meanwhile Sir Wilfred was busy seeking donations for an even bigger orphanage at St. Anthony to take care of the coast's hundreds and hundreds of destitute children.

Mina saw many instances of generosity that heartened her. Esther Campbell, a girl of twelve years, came up the bay from Mulligans that winter, principally to get clothing if possible from the clothing store. She asked Mina for outfits to clothe only her brothers and sisters, nothing for herself. But Mina did not let her go away without some wool stockings and dresses and material to make a parka and mitts. Many years later, when Esther was a married woman living next door to Mina in North West River, with children of her own to clothe, Mina used to tease her about the little girl who wanted underwear and jackets for everyone except herself.

Cartwright had been terribly hurt by the flu. They had no hospital, no doctor or nurse to care for them, and many died who need not if only help had been available and so many hadn't been sick at once. The North West River people were well aware how fortunate they had been to have only two deaths, and sorry for the Cartwrighters, many of whom were friends or relatives. They decided to put on a fair for the benefit of Cartwright villagers. Though they had very little to give in that poverty-stricken, hard pressed year of little fur and much sickness, they fashioned presents and mitts and moccasins and box lunches and bought and sold among one another to the amount of four hundred dollars, which they sent to Reverend Gordon to use for helping Cartwright widows and orphans as he thought best.

It was an immense sum for them to have raised. Even more important, it represented the first all-out community effort the widely scattered hunter-fisher families of Hamilton Inlet had ever joined together to accomplish. They were beginning to speak of themselves with pride as Labradorean, something quite different from Newfoundlanders or livyers, and at last Doctor Paddon's hope that they might achieve some feeling of political and economic entity was beginning to bear fruit. They had always helped one another in the most amazing and self-sacrificing ways. Maybe at last some representation could be won for Labrador in the government of Newfoundland, which ruled but so seldom aided them.

It is sad that Dr. Harry Paddon did not live to see the subsequent link-up with Canada in 1949, when the Crown Colony of Newfoundland achieved provincial status. But Mina did, and she was especially glad in the midst of high-powered governmental reorganizations that now those mothers she loved so dearly could send away to Canada and not have to pay heavy customs duty on the needles and thread and wool and jackets they needed for their children and their men, and even for themselves.

THE LONG CROSSING

PART 1

DEEP IN THE LABRADOR WILDERNESS three men gaunt
with hunger sat staring into a campfire. A cold wind stirred the
embers. Waves pounded the beach of the big lake beside them—
waves that made canoe travel impossible and had already pinned
them to this shore for three days. It had taken them all summer to
struggle this far, up rapids, around falls, through chains of lakes,
across bogs, and over scores of hilly or mountainous portages
without a trail.

The leader of the expedition was Leonidas Hubbard, of New
York, an editor of the magazine *Outing*. The second was also a
New Yorker, Dillon Wallace, who later wrote a number of books
of northern travel and yarns for boys, such as *Ungava Bob* and
Grit a-Plenty. The third was George Elson, a part-Indian guide
whom Hubbard had hired from the Missanabie River district of
James Bay.

Now they were midway of their proposed journey from North
West River village to Ungava Bay, hundreds of miles from nowhere,
their food practically gone. All this day they had eaten nothing but
a few cranberries. Their summer gear was worn thin, their boots
were falling to pieces, and winter in this northern land was baring
its claws. The night was September 15, 1903.

"Boys," said Hubbard suddenly, "what do you say to turning
back?"

It was a decision that had long been in their minds. Already they were getting weak, subsisting on what trout they could get (and eating the entrails), an occasional rabbit, now and then some partridges or a duck or goose. There was seldom enough for the three of them. But they had suffered so much in their drive to traverse the country and come out at its northern rim that their minds still fought against giving up. "I came to go with you," said George Elson, the guide, "and I want to do what you do." Wallace at first opposed the return, and then said it was best.

George Elson is the hero of this tale of three trips and many lives. You must picture him as a dark and handsome man, on the tall side, in a black felt hat and threadbare clothes. He spoke good English and was supremely kind, strong, and loyal. It is impossible to know what a guide is thinking, since he seldom writes books or keeps a journal. It is plain, however, that Elson made the campfires in the rain, put up the tent, carried the canoe on innumerable long portages even in winds that twisted him sidewise. He was extraordinarily skillful with pole and tracking-line ascending rapids, and equally good at running them or deciding when they were too rough to run. He was the sharp-eyed hunter who killed most of the meat. Without him, Hubbard and Wallace would not have come this far, and would have had no chance of getting back. He was far from his home on Hudson Bay and had never seen this particular area before. He had said a long time previous to this that the season was getting late and their margin of safety too thin. Now he faced the classic dilemma of guides, whose code dictates that they go into the wilderness as far as a party wishes, and then that they come out with the party or don't come out at all. At least one Labrador guide has died on the height-of-land for such reasons. Never in a lifetime of his own solitary hunting and trapping had George found himself in such a tight spot as this.

It was a genuine feeling for wildness that had brought all three men to this particular beach on this particular evening. Labrador in 1903, no planes flying over, no Goose Bay Airport, no iron being mined, scarcely any good maps, nobody but a few Montagnais and Naskapi Indians in the interior, was a land of mystery. It was much wilder than Alaska, with which it has frequently been confused. In distant New York, this huge unknown with its intricate crisscross of streams and brooding lakes full of beauty and danger had exerted an irresistible pull on Hubbard. He was already a considerable traveler. Following his recent marriage to a beautiful trained nurse, he and his young wife had spent a five-month honeymoon wandering the byways of the Southern Appalachian mountains in Tennessee and North Carolina, from which he had garnered two articles for the *Atlantic Monthly*. In February 1902, he had been snowshoeing in northern Quebec with Montagnais Indian trappers, gathering material for the book *Children of the Bush*. He had made other trips along the wild north shore of Lake Superior.

Not long after his return from Quebec, the Labrador dream seized him. "The Montagnais and Naskapi Indians of the upper George River," he told his wife, "are probably the most primitive Indians left on the North American continent. They dress in skins and live at the edge of the barren grounds. I want to see the caribou migrations and the wild lakes." He would make a six-hundred-mile canoe-and-portage journey northward through the Labrador peninsula. He would leave the trapper village of North West River at the head of Hamilton Inlet. He would go up Grand Lake and from it find an old Indian route via the Naskaupi River into Lake Michikamau, a body of water so vast the Indians said that you couldn't see across it and that its waters sank below the horizon. Somewhere beyond Michikamau's myriad bays and islands, they would find a north-flowing current that would be the start of a three-hundred-mile run down the George. Whether the George River was full of rapids or a smooth water-highway he did not know. "We'll find out when we get there," he said. "The trip will take all summer, and we'll have to travel fast to get out before freeze-up." At the mouth of the George, on Ungava Bay, was a Hudson's Bay Company post. If they could get there early enough, they might catch the once-a-year supply vessel that was returning south in the autumn; if not, they would have to winter at Ungava.

Hubbard had been married only two years and hated leaving his wife, Mina. She traveled north with him and his friend Wallace as far as Battle Harbour, at the southern corner of Labrador on the Straits of Belle Isle. There she had to take the steamer southward, while he went on north aboard another craft. It was a sad parting in the rain in that rock-girt harbor where Indians and Eskimos once waged war long ago. As Mina Hubbard said in the book she later wrote, he had a vision of the wilderness that would not let him rest. This vision illuminated their parting, which was fortunate, because they would never see each other again. That grim day in the rain, it never occurred to Mrs. Hubbard that she would be the first to complete the long trek to Ungava.

Hubbard and Wallace and Elson left the snug little trapper village of North West River in an eighteen-foot canoe, with a minimum of gear. Three in a canoe is not a good arrangement for crucial journeys, as trappers know, since the third man means 160 pounds less grub the canoe can carry—and he eats too. One wonders what Elson thought, for he certainly knew this fundamental of iron-hard wilderness logistics. They were told that fish won't bite in the autumn when the days grow cold, and so they must have a gill net to be set in the shallows for food. But when the starvation time came their net was so old and rotten they had to throw it away.

A number of men could have guided them the first fifty miles on their way, but none was hired. The three paddled happily up the thirty-five miles of Grand Lake's blue expanse, with wooded headlands looking down on them, and took a stream which they thought was the Naskaupi River at its head. A dozen local trappers could have started them correctly on the Naskaupi River, but already the party had missed it and was astray. They were on a little stream known as Susan's Brook, not the Naskaupi at all. The stream soon narrowed to fast rapids and cascades where they struggled in ice water to the waist or portaged on the rocks or pulled their hearts out on the tracking line. Here and there they found a blaze, or blackened rocks where Indians had had a winter camp, and these signs confirmed the hope that they were on the route to Michikamau.

The mosquitos, no-see-ums, and black flies were beyond belief. Wallace became ill, and Hubbard was so sick he could not eat or travel. They recovered somewhat and pressed on, frequently in rain. Often they must leave the rough "river," portaging all day through gullies and swamps and over brushy ridges, making as little as two-and-a-half miles before collapsing in the next camp. Already they were beginning to jettison some of their gear. Evenings, they had to scout ahead for a course. Some fifteen days out of North West River village they reached a point where another good-sized stream came into the Susan. Which branch should they ascend? Scouting ahead on the south, or left-hand branch, George found a blaze and the rotten poles of an old Indian wigwam, which convinced Hubbard they were on the route to Michikamau. There-

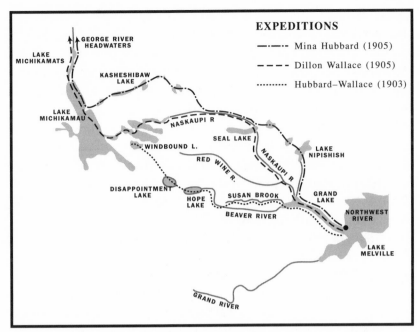

Map 3   The separate routes taken across southern Labrador toward the George River by the three Hubbard and Wallace expeditions.

fore, leaving the valley of the Susan and slogging up the branch they christened "Goose Creek," they were soon disappointed to meet more rapids that had to be portaged. Already short of grub, they killed four geese and rejoiced that night in a big feed by their evening campfire. Then their branch branched again, leading to two lakes they called Mountaineer and Elson.

Since Lake Elson provided all the trout they could eat and the best fishing they had encountered, a two-day camp was established by its shore for drying forty-five large fish. Beyond this camp they discovered a larger river, the Beaver. Hoping it might come from Michikamau, they hoisted the canoe and their packs on their backs once more and made the two-mile cross-over portage to the Beaver.

Soon it too worsened, and then they were on the plateau among the watery mazes. Here are lakes, islands, bays, swamps, rivers, brooks, ponds, and streams so limitless that one could not know one thousandth part of them. Already by August 11, they were down to forty pounds of flour, eight pounds of tea, twenty pounds of pea meal, a little sugar, bacon, baking powder, dried apple, and a bit of rice. Their clothes were disintegrating into rags, and Hubbard's and Wallace's boots were wearing out. Still struggling up chains of brooks, waterfalls, cascades, rapids, little ponds, bogs, and hills, they sometimes made no more than a mile and a half a day. Mosquitos and flies on the portages covered them with blood, made their wrists burn continuously, puffed their ears, and swelled their eyes almost shut. They fought on up the impossible streams till their weariness made them too faint to care. The carries were so terrible that they again lightened their loads by caching some of the already scant supplies. They would hunt. They would get caribou and bear. Occasionally they shot a few partridges, some geese, or yellowlegs. Hubbard was an ardent fisherman, and perhaps it was that that entrapped them. Evening after evening he caught trout by a riffle or a cascade while the other two made soup or portaged on another hundred yards. Diarrhea weakened them. They had many, many days of cold rain that kept them in camp eating up their precious food and making no miles. They also lost much time scaling rocky, brush-covered hills from whose crests they studied the country, trying to guess the route to choose through the labyrinth of waterways and hills.

It was a great moment the day that Hubbard and Elson scouted to the top of a small mountain and saw Michikamau at last, the great lake, the will-o-the-wisp they could not capture, still far away. North of them a series of lake expansions apparently ran into the lake. Perhaps there was a water connection. They would hunt it. If they found no connection, they would portage some more. With Michikamau just beyond, they could stand some more portaging, they said.

So they paddled east, looking for an opening, but found none—only a glimpse of what they thought was a bay of Michikamau. It rained and was cold. Hubbard shot a partridge for supper with his .22 pistol. The rain beat down. They climbed another mountain and could not see a way. Now, with autumn's cold weather, the fishing was poor. "If we only had a trout net," Hubbard wrote in his journal, "we would be O.K." The shadow of bad trouble was deepening over them. But they would push on. They would get to the Naskapi country and the caribou. Almost daily their plans changed now as to which way to go and what to do.

They climbed another mountain and could see no feasible route. They found a good-sized stream falling into their lake from the south. But it was too shoal and rapid for progress. They caught one of the great lake trout known as *naymaycush* and some smaller trout. But in the night some animal stole their giant *naymaycush*. They had only flour enough for two meals. And gales kept the white-capped seas racing across their "Windbound Lake." That was the night, September 15, with the icy wind spitting sleet and the waves roaring beside them, when they made the momentous decision to turn back.

But returning to Grand Lake and the safety of North West River village was not easy. Hubbard's plan here beside Windbound Lake was to hunt and fish with the utmost vigor, in order to stock up food for "the 30-mile portage" of hills and ponds and streams that lay immediately behind them. Snow fell and the autumn gales blew on, and they could not get enough even for their day-to-day needs. Sitting late by a roaring campfire, their only comfort, Hubbard looked into the coals and saw his wife's lovely face. "Have thought a good deal about home," he wrote in his diary. "It seems to me I'll never be willing to leave it again. I don't believe I'll want any more trips too hard for Mina to share. Her companionship and our home life are better than a great trip. So it seems to me."

They fell full length in bogs with their loads, weakened by the work and the scant meals of berries and a little erbswurst, with occasionally a few spoonfuls of pea meal. Snow covered the ground, and the nights were getting bitter. For the first time, they rolled up together in the blankets for warmth. It was September 24, and they should have been out of the country long before this. But George shot a goose, and that kept them going on this thirty-mile chain where they carried the canoe more than it carried them. Then Hubbard shot a duck; he caught seventy pounds of trout and they rejoiced. They rested in camp, cooking and drying fish, restoring their strength. But there is an old saying that you get weak on trout. Hubbard couldn't carry the canoe on September 29.

Back they slogged over the height-of-land, seeing their old camps, remembering the lakes they had named. Evening after evening Hubbard fished for trout, twenty here, fifty there. He was fishing for his life. The fish were small and soon gone. The only comfort was the campfire at night, where they toasted themselves and planned the magnificent repasts they would eat when they got out to civilization. They were all the best of pals, each helping the other, never quarreling; and they would lie under a tarpaulin in the rain beside the bright fire, holding out their hands to the blaze, and tell each other stories of boyhood and the events that had shaped their lives. Hubbard wrote that Wallace was a great comfort to him on those evenings. Wallace had it figured out that even on the steamer journey home they would rent rooms in St. John's, Newfoundland, where they changed steamships and could cook their own meals: rich, bone-building stews, rice and gravy, plenty of beef. Hubbard described to them the bounty of his childhood Michigan farm home, and said that George must visit him and his wife for a long, long time at their Congers, New York, home. For supper they would have turkey roasted and stuffed like a goose, potatoes, bannocks made while the turkey was roasting, one of George's most excellent puddings, coffee, and maple creams.

On October 11 they reached a place where they had killed a caribou on the way up. George gathered up the bones and two hoofs, pounded them and boiled them, and though the ensemble was maggoty, they had three cups of greasy broth each.

Next day they ran several bad rapids, and ate boiled bones, roasted hoofs, and part of a caribou nose. The three of them could scarcely carry the canoe a hundred feet around part of a rapid too rough to run. That night they boiled and ate one of the caribou-skin moccasins that Hubbard had made himself, sharing it three ways and drinking the water it was boiled in. Next day they were too weak to carry the canoe around a little fall and had to drag it. George shot a whiskeyjack (bluejay), which they washed down with bone broth and tea. George, the redoubtable George, who did the hunting and was the mainstay, had a bad back, an old touch of recurring lumbago that had before this crippled him till he couldn't crawl. In their already desperate situation it must have seemed to him the last straw. That night he said if he didn't feel better by morning, Hubbard and Wallace had better go on and try to make their way without him.

But with the morning he found himself slightly improved, and shooting a duck just before noon made him feel better yet. At noon as they ate the duck, they faced an all-important decision. They had reached the familiar place where their "Big River" (the Beaver) swung close to the Goose Creek cross-over and the smaller stream they had ascended from Grand Lake. Should they cross over on their own tracks and take the known smaller stream (Susan's Brook), which was bad water nearly all the way to the mouth? It

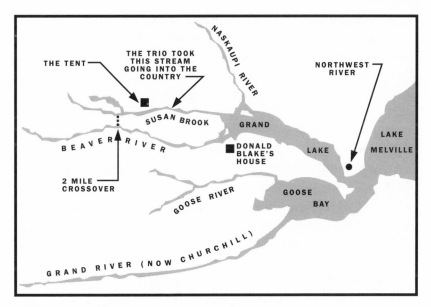

Map 4   The 1903 Hubbard-Wallace expedition, searching for the Naskaupi River route to Lake Michikamau, missed the entrance to the river, concealed by an island at its mouth, and headed up Susan Brook instead.

was a series of portages over which they could not hope to carry the canoe, they were so weak. Or should they try the "big river" they were on (the Beaver River), which ran out they knew not where? They juggled their own lives in their hands as they sat by the water's edge, watching the silver and black current purl through the stones and slide across sands that had been rocks many thousands of years ago.

As often happens among men who live lonely lives in northern Canada, George had had a dream about this crucial choice of routes. The question had, of necessity, been planted in his subconscious mind; and his subconscious mind, uncluttered by the litter that dims "educated" mentalities, had worked on it while he slept. To him had come a man who told him, "Don't leave the river. Follow the river down. It is the only way you can save your lives."

Wallace apparently favored the big river too. Hubbard, on the other hand, thought perhaps it ran out at Goose Bay and they might starve on some lonely shore at its mouth. He had seen so many rough unnavigable streams, he thought this was only another. He knew now they had no leeway for a single misstep.

Thus, he chose what Labradormen called Susan's Brook, the smaller stream they knew, "the terrible valley," as Wallace later dubbed it. Probably what swayed Hubbard was part of a bag of flour they had cached partway down the small stream, and farther down a little lard and milk. As usual, the other two deferred without question to Leonidas, who was the originator and leader of the expedition. Theirs was a discipline self-originated, self-maintained, and stronger than flesh and bone.

Consequently, they left the canoe beside the Beaver and retraced their own route two miles back across to the familiar Susan, intent on following it down. They never knew whether they had made the correct life-and-death decision. Certain it is that the Beaver, flowing out to Grand Lake, came close to the cabin-home of Donald Blake, where food and help were available. George Elson and Wallace and Hubbard never knew whether they could have negotiated the downstream rapids of the Beaver.

Now that they were leaving the canoe and starting their final dash down the Susan for Grand Lake afoot, it was time to jettison all remnants. George urged that they be ruthless about it and travel, travel, travel, whether they could carry anything or not.

Each day, as they staggered down the small rough stream, they left behind more gear to lighten their packs: one day the sextant box, artificial horizon, and a fishing rod; another day a rifle, cleaning rod, cartridges, the sextant, and fifteen films. During these and preceding days, Hubbard's journal is sprinkled with brief reminiscences and longings, together with notations of the day's decreasing mileage and its meal of bones, berries, ducks, fish or boiled caribou hide, if any.

> All day I have been thinking about childhood things and the country. I want to get in touch with it again. I want to go to Canada, if possible, for Christmas. I want to go somewhere in sugar making. So homesick for my sweetheart. Fairly strong despite short grub.

> Rain drove us from our campfire just as George declared, 'Now we'll talk about French toast, and what we'll eat when we get to New York.' So we all crawled into blankets and did plan and plan good dinners.

> All talking about home, all happy to be going there.

All sat late by campfire talking and thinking of home.

I'm weak and nervous. . . Wallace notices it. Have not taken bath for two weeks, ashamed of my ribs which stick out like skeletons.

All talk much of home now. At campfire George told me of his plans to get married and his love story.

Thinking much of home and M., and our plans and old friends . . . I am aching to write some sketches and stories that have come to my mind. We talk much of future plans, and the campfire continues to be a glorious meeting place.

Oh, to see my sweetheart and be home again!

One night toward the middle of October, sitting by the fire, Hubbard said, "Mrs. Hubbard this evening will now be at dinner, and after her meal will finish with a lot more on the table. Oh, if she could only hand me a piece of bread!"

The day before, George had found two old goose heads and some bones at a former camp, all of which they boiled or charred, and ate. He also found three tiny slices of bacon in an old lard can, and they were mighty good. Next afternoon, Hubbard began to shake and could not walk. Wallace came back and took his pack. George encouraged him on to a place about forty yards ahead where they could camp, then hurried to make a fire and prepare him tea. All the food they were carrying consisted of just over a pound of pea meal and a little tea.

For breakfast next morning they had one partridge that George had shot. Thus fortified, Hubbard was able to go on. George had one good suit of underwear that he had been saving till the weather grew even colder. At noon he threw away everything belonging to him, including the underwear. He felt too weak to take off the bad and put on the good. But in the afternoon as they were resting, he spotted a caribou following a small tributary stream down toward them. They all fell flat and kept still, hoping for a shot. Unfortunately, they were upwind, and the caribou smelled them, stood a moment and trotted off. George took out across a marsh to head him off. With all the power of his will George battled his weakness and ran. But when he reached the other side, the caribou was gone. Slowly he retraced his steps. Though he had been away some time, he found the two still lying where he had left them, with their faces pressed to the ground, and they did not speak until he spoke to them. He made them some tea, and they went on. That night he got the tent up but hadn't strength for chopping wood—just broke sticks.

October 17 they followed the river all day with nothing to eat. Hubbard's weakness was such that he could scarcely speak. At evening he could not go any farther. George took his pack and encouraged him on about twenty yards to a good dry place where they had camped before on the way up. Then he made a fire and gave Hubbard hot tea and a cup of pea meal. It was Hubbard's last day of travel.

Again, as at Windbound Lake and the bend of the big river, a time of decision was upon them. Each time, the margin of choice narrowed like a closing door. In fact, at this last council there was no alternative; they were making their last bid. The little bag of flour they had cached was still ten miles downstream. They spoke openly of the chances of getting out alive, and the chances were not good. It was decided that Wallace and George would press on to the flour. If they found it, George, as the strongest, would take some (*you must take the most because you will be traveling,* Hubbard said) and go on to North West River for aid, hoping to meet trappers on his way. Wallace would return the ten miles to Hubbard with part of the flour, and together they would try to keep alive at the tent till rescuers came.

That evening was a sad one, no talk of homelands or big meals. Hubbard told George that Mrs. Hubbard was to have his journal. *If I starve and you get out,* Hubbard said, *tell her how things were and that I didn't suffer much. If you come upon some trappers, send them with grub and don't try to come yourself, because you'll be too weak. We will be right here, so you'll know where to send them. If things go badly for me, the Hudson's Bay Company manager at North West River will help you and keep you all winter. I will write a letter to him.*

To both men he said he was sorry to have brought them to such a state—that it was his work and not theirs, and but for him they would not be so close to death.

George told him not to be troubled. "If we didn't want to come, we would have stayed home. So don't put the blame on yourself."

Hubbard and Elson slept soundly, while Wallace kept on a fire and wrote a farewell letter to his sisters, to be left at the tent. The tent was the thing, they all felt, that would eventually be found if they perished.

In the morning Hubbard was weaker than ever, utterly unable to travel. There was not much to divide, and the two who were leaving could scarcely carry anything. They planned to go without even a blanket for the freezing nights, but Hubbard convinced them they should tear up the wool and take at least a piece each, leaving him with a double one. He also prevailed on them to take the pea meal and a little tea, since all depended on their success. Hubbard took his .22 pistol off his belt and pressed it upon George saying, "I will have the rifle if I have anything to shoot." Wallace already had a pistol. They left Hubbard with a little tea, some mouldy lumps sticking to a flour bag they had found here, and a moccasin whose neighbor they had already eaten. His tent was pitched against a rock to reflect heat. There was firewood cut. Shedding tears, they each knelt and kissed his sunken, bearded cheek. "Good-bye, I'll try to come back soon," Wallace said.

George said, "The Lord help us, Hubbard. With His help I'll save you if I can get out."

It was time to go.

So they turned down the lonely river where the coves were icing on the black water in a freezing sleet storm.

Ten miles was an almost infinite distance for men in their condition. And would the flour be there? And could they find it? All day the sleet and wet and wind beat at them. They tripped and fell over the smallest obstructions and were a long time getting up. Whenever they went near a little tree, it seemed to reach out its branches at them and knock them down. They had gone perhaps half way when night closed in. They had no ax for a night fire and no shelter. They were in an old forest-fire burn where game was scarce. The rotten wood that they pulled together smoldered and smoked and blinded them. In the night it snowed. Knee-deep, they staggered on in the morning. Their eyes were troubling them from the smoke, and everything looked blue. George got a shot at a partridge, but missed. Then they came to the only shallow place, where George remembered they had to ford the river because the flour was on the other side and still a long way down. There was nothing for it but to go into the cold, icy water up to their waists.

Having crossed, they made a fire and had a cup of tea, then started off again as soon as they could. In the afternoon the weather cleared up, but the snow began to drift, and everything was freezing hard as evening clamped down.

Wallace was near his finish, and could not keep up. Just before dark, George waited till he came near.

"How far yet to the flour?" Wallace asked.

"About two miles."

"Go on while it is yet light," Wallace told him, "and see if you can find the flour; because if you cannot get there tonight maybe you will not be able to go any further should we live to see the morning."

"Yes," said George, "that was what I was going to tell you, and the reason why I waited."

He started off again, and within about forty yards came across a partridge, which he shot and killed with the pistol Hubbard had given him. Wallace came up, and the two men sat together eating part of it raw. "Go on again," said Wallace, and George did, but soon he came to a mass of caribou trails where he knew Wallace would get tangled in the late twilight. So he stayed and waited, and they sat down together and ate some more of the partridge. Now they staggered on together in the darkness. "How far is it to the flour?" Wallace kept asking.

Late in the night, George knew they were coming to the place. There was no mark; they had just thrown away the partially filled bag, never thinking they would ever come past here again. George put down his little load.

"Is this the place?" Wallace said.

"Yes," said George, and went to the spot, dug in the snow, and pulled out the bag. There were perhaps eight or nine pounds, one solid lump, black with mold. They broke off bits with their knives, ate some and found it good. They could not remember how long they had been without bread, and craving farinaceous food. But for the killed partridge, they would never have reached the flour.

They made a fire, finished the partridge and had some flour soup, wishing with all their hearts that Hubbard could be sharing. Wallace's eyes were troubling him still from the smoke of the night before. George kept on a fire all night, deeply worried that Wallace might not be able to get back with the flour. For breakfast they ate some more of the black flour soup. In his dash for the village and help, George would take only two pounds of it with him, despite Wallace's remonstrances. "I will trust in getting game in the wooded country soon," he said. He gave Wallace six or seven pounds, so that the latter would have the strength to get back with some of it to Hubbard and the tent. "Don't leave the river, remember to stay by the river or you will get lost," the guide warned. They said farewell on a barren ridge where the view was open, and as the distance widened, they kept calling, "Good-bye, good-bye," for they did not know whether they would see each other again.

It snowed hard all day, but George slogged on, trying to make time now that he had a little flour soup in his belly. In the afternoon he killed a porcupine, and how he wished he could give some to the boys! No doubt he singed off the quills, as is the custom. In the night, snow fell again, so that the going was very heavy for George without snowshoes. That afternoon he killed another porcupine. Next day it was snowing hard again, and cold. He made a fire at noon to patch his shoepacks but couldn't spare the time for boot mending. Sometimes he left the river, it was so crooked. The snow was deep and the country very rough. He knew the hours were running out and found it hard to rest, though he was so done he could hardly put one foot in front of the next. If he stopped even for five minutes, fancies and phantoms crowded into his mind. Perhaps they were self-doubts that he wasn't doing his best, wasn't covering the miles. At any rate, going on seemed to exorcise them. In the darkness by his fire he tried to rest and drive away the fancies by saying over and over, aloud in the icy air, "Because it is night therefore I cannot travel, because it is night therefore I cannot travel."

Snow again next day, October 23. In the afternoon it turned mild, wet, sticky, soaking him to the skin. His hands were always cold, falling among the rocks in the snow with no mitts. He cut off the sleeves of his undershirt, tied up the ends with cord, and put them on for mitts. Several times that day he had a notion of giving up because of the deep snow. And again the phantoms and mental images came to him. Then he would get up and go on. If he fell, he was going to fall forward; if he died, he was going to die crawling.

He came to the place where they had left coffee and milk, found the coffee, but no milk. That evening he killed four partridges. It was very cold, and he found it difficult to dry his clothes, having no ax for fire-building.

Saturday the 24th he reached the place where they had left three pounds of lard in a pail, and found it with that uncanny skill of his. He still had some porcupine (never throwing away the bones), several partridges, and a little flour. He put his food under his head and slept. But first he sang a hymn in the darkness:

> The night is dark, and I am far from home;
> Lead Thou me on.

By the fire, with the hundreds of miles of winter night around him, George was singing out his song. It is often so with trappers far away in the solitudes. The song is not very musical; it is more like a shout.

Sunday the 25th, snow was falling again. He killed four more partridges with Hubbard's .22 pistol and pushed on over high mountains through the almost waist-deep whiteness. Next morning at about ten o'clock he came out at last to Grand Lake and thought he would make good time along its shores to the village of North West River. After only two miles, he saw with horror a river-mouth barring his way, and he with no ax for making a raft. Ice was drifting down on the swift current. In despair he followed up the river of steep banks and fast current, looking for a crossing, and came to a fork. There was one stream here then, he reasoned, and two at the lake shore. It would be better to cross the one stream above the fork. This he tried all afternoon, but it was impossible. Sadly he gave up, and went down to the lake shore again, where he stood, watching the ice float past. Perhaps it was not too deep. Perhaps, since he couldn't do any better, he might wade part of it and swim the rest. Into the numbing water he went, with ice bumping him, cramps knotting his legs, and paralysis seizing his whole body. The paralysis enveloped him, and, turning back before midstream, he was barely able to get out in time. There he stood, at the head of the thirty-five-mile lake, forty miles from North West River, with the great blue hills looking down at him and darkness coming again. Maybe he would never cross, just starve there. Anyhow, he made a fire and ate. All night the sound of the rubbing, drifting ice troubled him. If only he had a canoe!

No sooner had daylight come than he tried to wade and swim the stream again, with the same result in the piercing cold. There was no way out but to try to make a raft of driftwood; this he did, cutting his tumpline in two pieces to bind two corners, using his belt for a third and a small piece of salmon twine for the fourth. The wind was blowing hard. Despite the long pole he carried, current and drifting ice took him out into the lake, where the wind caught and carried him. The raft was breaking up in the heavy sea, so he lay down in the icy water with the waves washing over him and held it together with his arms. Thus he drifted for nearly two hours, sure it was his end. Then the wind drove him near a long point where his pole could touch—the pole that he had clung to while consciousness ebbed.

He was ashore again, and glad. But there was still the other branch to cross, and this one was much wider. No driftwood had lodged by this stream mouth, so he pulled down rotten stumps and gathered together whatever deadwood he could find, not a dry stitch on him, clothes stiffening in the winter weather, telling himself he would not make a fire till he had crossed this second barrier. This raft was much larger than the other. It was built on newly frozen ice so that he could launch it by breaking the ice around it with his pole. Talking aloud to himself all the time, encouraging himself, telling himself how fine a raft it was and how proud he was, he poled out into the channel and got across safe without much trouble after all. Then and there he picked a place for his night camp and shot three partridges on the spot, as though it were a good omen. There was a point just beyond, and round the point a deep bay. Before it got dark and he made his fire, he thought he would just look around the point and into the bay, in case there were any more rivers. Suddenly he spied a small boat, and ran toward it, thinking he could use it to sail down the lake to the post. Then he saw the roof of a house. A child screamed and a girl ran in the door terrified at the sight of him all wet and haggard and half barefoot. It was the head-of-the-lake home of trapper Donald Blake and his family.

The kindly and wide-eyed Mrs. Blake bustled about the cabin, getting him a bed and dry clothes and food. But he could not sleep until he had arranged with Donald and his brother that they should leave with food and clothes for Wallace and Hubbard at the earliest possible instant. He learned from the Blakes that the whole summer's bitter travel had been not on the Naskaupi River chain at all. Naskaupi mouth, masked by islands, lay miles across on the other side of the lake. They had followed an unnavigable torrent known as Susan's Brook. And their "Big River" was Beaver River, a slightly better stream but by no means easy traveling.

Donald and his young brother, Gilbert (about whom more later), went off in the night in their boat to pick up two more men seven miles away, Allen Goudy and Duncan McLean. Early in the morning the four Labradormen set off into the country with grub, snowshoes, boots, and extra clothes. Elson had made them a map, but that was scarcely necessary, for they knew this country like the palm of their hands and they were talking to a man like themselves.

They found Wallace one mile above the place where he had left George. He had a little flour and he was alive but he couldn't travel. He had shot nothing. They followed his tracks and saw where he had crossed Susan's Brook, camped within a few hundred yards of the tent, and been unable to find it, confused by the new snow and his eyes half blind. He said he thought he had gone beyond the tent, and so turned back and wandered downstream to the place where they found him.

Hubbard was dead in the tent. He had made his last entry in his journal and written a letter to his wife the day they left him. Three or four caribou had wandered round and round the tent, but there were no man-tracks in the snow. His last writings in his notebook read:

> I want to say here that they are two of the very best, bravest, and grandest men I ever knew, and if I die it will not be because they did not put forth their best efforts. . . . I am not so greatly in doubt as to the outcome. I believe they will reach the flour and be strengthened, that Wallace will reach me, that George will find Blake's cache and camp and send help. So I believe we will all get out.

> My tent is pitched in open tent style in front of a big rock. The rock reflects the fire, but now it is going out because of the rain. I think I shall let it go and close the tent, till the rain is over, thus keeping out wind and saving wood. To-night or tomorrow perhaps the weather will improve so I can build a fire, eat the rest of my moccasins and have some bone broth. Then I can boil my belt and oil-tanned moccasins and a pair of cowhide mittens. They ought to help some. I am not suffering. The acute pangs of

hunger have given way to indifference. I am sleepy. I think death from starvation is not so bad. But let no one suppose that I expect it. I am prepared, that is all. I think the boys will be able with the Lord's help to save me.

While the four men were gone, George paced the shore by the Blakes' winter cabin, sick in his soul with wondering what the news would be, sick in his body too from eating only a few baking-powder biscuits with butter and molasses that hospitable Mrs. Blake had pressed upon him the evening he staggered in. But sick or not, George shot partridges during those days to keep the lonely family in meat.

When he came to Donald Blake's, George had six partridges and a piece of porcupine, besides about half the flour he had carried away when he said goodby to Wallace; and for insurance he was also carrying all the bones of the porcupine. He had killed two porcupines and eleven partridges. He had traveled forty miles through the roughest kind of country, in deep snow without snowshoes, without a rifle, without an ax, without a tent. His clothing and his boots were falling to pieces. He was emaciated and exhausted beyond the point of endurance when he parted from Wallace, and all the food he had was two pounds of flour. Nevertheless, he arrived promptly. And despite the freezing nights and the rivers to ford, he arrived in better condition and with more food than when he departed. That is what it is to be a *hunter,* in the classic, original sense of the word.

Waiting, George wondered, *If Hubbard and Wallace are dead, will people say I left them, will they say I came out and saved myself?* It was an ugly question, touching his code for himself. He was saddened too at the thought of all the ill coincidences that had dogged them: that their map, which had many correct features on it, showed only one river entering the head of Grand Lake, right where Susan's Brook was, but labeled "Naskaupi River"; that nobody had thought to tell them of other streams; that Susan's Brook had a fork a dozen or so miles up, where the map had also shown a fork called the Red Wine River. It was like being dizzy, to discover they had been giving the right names to the wrong things all summer and autumn.

The men were unable to bring out Hubbard's body, it was so far and rough and the river not thoroughly frozen yet for a path, and they had Wallace to see to. But when they came, they brought Hubbard's diary and camera and rifle, and they also brought a letter, written as he lay dying, recommending George in the most sincere terms to the Hudson's Bay Company post manager. Even in death he had strengthened the bond between himself and George, and George, on his part said, "What a friend he was and what a brave man. I have seen a good many fine people in my time, but I have never seen a man like Hubbard and I never expect to see another."

The trappers thought a lot of George, and they were soon close friends. Delayed by snowstorms on the big lake, he and Wallace reached the village of North West River in a little sailing skiff on November 6. Wallace was taken into the Hudson's Bay Company manager's house and put to bed and tended by the housekeeper. He had weighed 170 pounds when he started out, and he now weighed 95. George, being part Indian, was in that day and age not welcomed in the manager's house. He was put up at the HBC "kitchen," where the Indians were required to stay when they came to trade. The little building was still there as late as 1942, by the rivermouth at the edge of the huge bay, a small red-roofed cabin, its wall-logs pinned together with old rifle barrels pounded into auger holes. It dated from the days when Donald Smith (Lord Strathcona) was a young man in charge of North West River post.

Wallace's toes were frozen and he had a bad time with them. He and George stayed in the head-of-the-bay settlements all winter. George was extremely popular with everyone. Wallace was not well liked. He seems to have had an unfortunate sense of class distinction which was hardly appropriate under the circumstances. He held aloof from trappers, and in his book called them "breeds."

It was during this time that friction began to develop between the two men. To bring out Hubbard's body George wished to go in early March when the winter snows had settled. Wallace repeatedly ordered him to bring out the canoe too. This meant that George could not get help from the local trappers, who were in any case busy with the all-important furring that provided their meager living for the whole coming year. They knew that the valley of the Susan was too rough for dog teams and that manhauling the body out on toboggans through the deep snow was all that could be done. As it turned out, the snow in there was from eight to twelve feet deep.

In March George set off, telling his reluctant helpers they needn't bring out the canoe, no matter what Wallace's injunctions were. It was a terrible trip, only three of them, one a faithful boy who plugged on despite broken snowshoes and a bad attack of snow-blindness. They had a steady succession of blizzards and bitter gales. It seems strange they did not have a dog team to help them the first forty miles to the head of Grand Lake.

Finding the tent all undisturbed, they went on farther up to see whether George could recover some of the gear that had been discarded in the last desperate days. And George did not disappoint them. Time after time he would stop, no mark, no sign, dig to the ground, and there it was. At five different places, some four to eight miles apart, he repeated this performance, uncovering five hundred cartridges, sextant, films and other articles. The last was in a marsh, without even a tree anywhere near. His two companions knew he could not do it this time. He wasn't sure himself, but he said he thought this was the place. He stopped. His two helpers each took a snowshoe and dug beside him, more from curiosity and consideration than anything else. Eight feet down, he began to feel around with his feet, and there was the little stump, and the bag hanging on it. Tom Blake, the older man, was stunned. "I been trappin'," he said, "ever since only a boy, and I wouldn't believe this if I didn't see it myself."

Back they started with the body, each man hauling a toboggan heavily loaded with the sad reminders, the boy Duncan McLean practically blind. New snow made the toboggans rimey so that they had to be turned up every mile and scraped with knives. Where swift rapids were unfrozen, they had only narrow borders of ice to go on, with steep mountains on either hand and no chance to leave the river.

Snow, snow, snow, every day, and the three small black specks crawling down the great white lake, hauling their loads, taking their turns ahead in the old old way.

George was received by Wallace with urgent orders to go back up and get the canoe. At this point Wallace was domineering and high-handed toward the guide whose endurance, skill, and courage had saved his life. Wallace was going to give the canoe to his host. Thus the HBC manager joined in exhorting George. George knew that the canoe would be crushed to pieces by the weight of

snow where they had left it by the riverbank in their desperate starvation time. He knew it was nonsense and a journey for nothing.
Furthermore, springtime was advancing and it was time they
started their dogteam journey down the coast to catch the first
steamer at Battle Harbor; no steamer would get into this bay till
July.

The canoe controversy grew like a thundercloud. George, who
had done so much already, said that it was Hubbard who had hired
him and that he and Hubbard had shared both in plans and pos-
sessions; thus the canoe was not Wallace's. Everything brought out
of the country had been brought out by the guide. "I do not have to
go up again," he said. "It is not long since I had my trip up there. I
think I have done my part." Nevertheless, Wallace continued to
order.

With dogs to help him up the lake, George prepared to go into
the country again. But storm after storm prevented a departure.
And then it was time to start south along the coast by dogteams
with the body, to catch the steamer.

Elson left the village two days early with a poor team of dogs and
the body in a spruce coffin. Everyone in the settlement turned out
to see him go, and some of the women wept. Wallace came later
with a good team and no load. Far down the bay, at Rigolet, where
they engaged new teams and teamsters, Elson had "the load" and
four dogs. Wallace traveled light with six. They were obviously no
longer comrades of the trail. Sledging from one poverty-stricken
hamlet to the next, hiring local guides and local teams, they found
dog feed short and people starving. But news of Elson had somehow filtered through already: "This is the man we heard of, when
he found everything he dug for in the snow this winter." The mission doctor at Battle Harbor had the load hermetically sealed in a
lead coffin, and May 28 poor Hubbard's much-traveled body was
buried in Monte Repose Cemetery, in Haverstraw, New York.

Wallace felt that the story of this tragic, epic journey should be
told. He put his version of it between the covers of a book called
The Lure of the Labrador Wild, which had a considerable vogue in
the States. He closed the book with these words: "Perhaps it is
God's will that I finish the work of exploration that Hubbard
began."

PART 2

HUBBARD'S YOUNG WIFE was crushed by his death. For many months during the autumn and early winter she had been hoping against hope, knowing how impossible communication was from the northern posts after freeze-up. It was not until January that she received the hideous message, "Mr. Hubbard died October 18 in the interior of Labrador."

Mina Hubbard was a tall and lovely person whose pictures remind one of a Gibson girl with a piled-up hairdo. She had taste and delicacy, and with it the fortitude and competence that are the crowning glory of some trained nurses. As she began to recover from the blow that fate had dealt her, the same idea took possession of her that filled Wallace's mind. She would finish the job her husband had commenced and make the trackless journey across Labrador to Ungava Bay.

She and Wallace did not join forces—far from it. She felt deeply estranged from him. She disliked his lack of consideration for George Elson. She was angry that Hubbard's films, recovered from the snow by Elson, were not given to her, but used instead by Wallace in *The Lure of the Labrador Wild.* Though his book paid many glowing tributes to Hubbard, there were things in it that deeply offended her. Perhaps Wallace pictured himself as more of a woodsman than he really was. She resented the fact that he did not reach the tent beside the Susan, and that her husband died, while Wallace lived. Quite possibly it was on the day early in 1905 when she first read Wallace's newly published book that her resolve crystallized to make the trip herself, publish her own tale, and with it her dead husband's journal and George Elson's sparse and geographically accurate version of what happened.

So it was that June 26, 1905, at the North West River post two canoe expeditions were packed and poised, ready to go. Mrs. Hubbard had two nineteen-foot canoes and a crew of four men led by George Elson, to whom she felt deeply attached for his loyalty to Hubbard and herself. The Wallace party was five in two canoes, one a nineteen-footer, the other eighteen feet. Also, trapper Duncan McLean accompanied Wallace's party in a rowboat. He was to be part of the expedition in its early stages and then return to the village. Wallace probably hired him to assure that the expedition took the correct river this time at the start. When Mrs. Hubbard and Wallace met along the sandy paths of that trapper village at the rivermouth beside the great Hamilton Inlet, it is quite possible they did not speak.

Wallace shoved off first. Next afternoon the village clustered around to say good-bye to Mrs. Hubbard, the HBC factor and the manager of the rival Revillon Frères "French post" outdoing each other in gallantries. She took her seat among the duffel amidships in Elson's canoe, dressed in a narrow-brimmed felt hat, sealskin boots, a long skirt over knickerbockers, and a sweater. Slung around her slender waist was a belt containing cartridges, revolver and a hunting knife. Many of the fine old part-Scots trappers who inhabit North West River wondered whether this pretty woman from outside would be alive when autumn came. But George, in his black hat, with his ever-reassuring smile was there.

Mrs. Hubbard's personal gear included camera equipment, sextant, artificial horizon, barometer, thermometer, high leather moccasins, a pair of sealskin slippers, three pairs duffel slippers, four suits of underwear, five pairs wool stockings, a rubber automobile shirt, a Swedish dogskin coat, leather gloves, woolen gloves, and a blouse for Sundays. She had an air mattress (crib size), one pair of blankets, a wool comforter weighing three and a half pounds, one little feather pillow, and a hot-water bottle. The rest of the party's outfit was exceedingly well planned, probably by George, and included a small balloon-silk tent for Mrs. Hubbard, plenty of guns, ammunition, pistols and knives, a fine selection of lightweight, nourishing grub, and an extra pair of shoe-packs for everybody.

Wallace did not go far the first two days. Mrs. Hubbard's men, by contrast, put their backs behind the paddles. Her departure was blessed by beautiful weather, the air clear as crystal, patches of snow still white on the hills and mountains, and a sky of big soft clouds, making a combination of green and blue and silver that brings homesickness to Labrador people if ever they go "outside." The Hubbard party had it calm on Grand Lake and paddled on and on lest the wind rise and make this notoriously rough lake impassable. At twilight they were nearing the vast cliffs of a headland that looks like a caribou with his nose immersed in the water. Ten o'clock, and still the dip-dip of paddles went on. Now and then they were laid across the gunnels and the pipes came out, just as with the oldtime voyageurs, who first unlocked the mysteries of Canada all the way to the Pacific. It was not till eleven that they turned ashore, the sky still light in the northwest, and made a roaring campfire, for the night had turned crisp. Resting only four hours, they embarked again at three A.M. and were safely in Naskaupi rivermouth at eight in the morning, where winds could not greatly trouble them.

There is no statement that it was a race, except that one of the chapters in Mrs. Hubbard's book, *A Woman's Way through Unknown Labrador,* is entitled "The Race for Ungava." According to Gilbert Blake, however, and the tales he told many years later, it was not pure accident that they left Wallace behind somewhere on Grand Lake that night. At any rate, they did not see Wallace and his party again for many a moon.

Bert Blake in 1905 was sixteen years old, a jolly, round-faced lad, already a capable hunter, as is the Labrador fashion, accustomed to rapids, canoes, and blizzards, accustomed even at that age to trapping alone in the bush in winter for weeks at a time. He had been one of the four rescuers who saved Wallace and tried to save Hubbard. Later to become the most famous guide in Labrador, he already knew Naskaupi River fifty miles up and was seething with joy to be part of such an expedition with the great George Elson. Within a day or two the pump for Mrs. Hubbard's air mattress was lost. Gilbert was glad, for then it was one of his jobs to inflate it for her with his breath each evening at the camp.

In its lower reaches the Naskaupi was so broad and deep that Mrs. Hubbard could not forget what it had cost to miss this stream two years before.

She was very proud of her four stalwart guides to whom she was entrusting her life. George had brought with him two others from the Missanabie country seven hundred miles west of Montreal. They were Joseph Iserhoff, of Russian and Indian parentage who spoke with a soft Scots accent, and Job Chapies, a pure-blood Cree who spoke only his native tongue. The fourth was the bright-eyed Gilbert Blake.

Some thirteen miles up the Naskaupi at the junction of the Red Wine River, they stopped and examined an Indian portage route which left the Naskaupi there for Seal Lake, avoiding the Naskaupi's heavy rapids above. The Naskaupi River flows from the great lake Michikamau via Seal Lake and many other lake expansions to Grand Lake. But much of the upper river is unnavigable, and there are numerous canoe and portage bypasses around stretches of rapids and falls. The guides examined the faint trail and decided to keep to the Naskaupi awhile. Before noon they came to Point Lucie, where Gilbert told them trappers leave their boats at the foot of the first rapid and haul toboggans forty miles overland in winter to Seal Lake. The river came pouring out from the foot of Mount Sawyer in a leaping, foaming torrent that was eating at ice-banks still twelve feet high. With crooked-knives the men shaved dry spruce poles and fitted iron "shods" brought from James Bay. Job soon proved a master hand at canoe-poling. The wilder the rapid, the better he seemed to like it. He would stand in the stern, his right foot back, left forward, leg against the thwart, with set pole holding the canoe steady in the rushing, roaring water while he looked over the way, choosing his course. Then he would move the canoe forward again, twisting its nose now this way, now that, in the most marvelous fashion, and when he drove it into the rush of water pouring around a big rock the pole would bend and tremble with the weight and strain he put on it. None of the others could compare with Indian Job at this art of poling.

Portaging along sand terraces eighty feet above the river's heavy rapids, Mrs. Hubbard got her first view of loads the men could carry. They camped that night two hundred feet above the river, and she tried to cook the baking-powder and flour bannocks for them, which they thought amusing, because she wasn't very good at it. Crossing the river in heavy breakers, they clawed their way up to Mountain Cat Lake, an expansion two miles long and half a mile wide with a current so swift they poled along its shores. Sunday camp was a blessed day of rest for washing, bathing, cooking, cutting hair. Mrs. Hubbard's feet were strained, and her face and hands were swollen and sore from mosquito bites but she did not complain.

It must have been a fast point where they had their first mishap, for two men were in the canoe poling and two men on the line tracking it, when the craft went bottom up. Job was almost drowned but they ran down alongshore and pulled him out. And he was soon laughing about his trip to the fishes and what he had seen down there. Most of the gear had been lashed in the canoe, but an extremely serious loss was all the axes, all the frying pans, a crooked-knife, and all the extra pole-shods. Worst of all was to face so long a journey without an ax. Could it be done? Mrs. Hubbard wondered whether the men would say they must turn back, but the idea did not occur to them.

Wading, dragging, poling, tracking, carrying across slippery boulders or tangled windfalls, they fought up the swift Naskaupi, sometimes making only two miles a day. Ungava seemed a long way off, and whether they could catch the late-August supply vessel there seemed extremely doubtful.

Never had the Labrador bush seen anything quite like Mrs. Hubbard walking across the innumerable portages, a tall figure in hat, mosquito veil, a full skirt, a white collar at her neck, sealskin boots, the pistol and knife at her belt. If the hellish clouds of mosquitos on hot still days, or the cold nights, or the ominous roar of rapids or the boulder-strewn shores she had to clamber along ever ruffled her serenity, she well concealed the fact. One night the lemmings ate three holes in her hat.

July 6 they reached Seal Islands expansion, another fast-moving lake, where Donald Blake's winter hunting tilt was built. It was a tiny log house near the river, under the spruces, surrounded by chips and the skeletons of martens from last winter's catch. There was a low doorway, no window, no floor, a log bunk, and a tin stove. Hanging on cross beams were covered pails containing rice, flour, beans, lard and a few candles. They took some lard and candles, leaving part of their two hundred pounds of bacon in its stead. There was no ax, though Gilbert looked and looked. He did get here, however, his own little frying pan and a small pail to add to the depleted cooking-ware department.

Rain drenched them late that afternoon and held them in camp all next day. They pushed down dead trees for their fire and burned them in half.

The river was practically all rapids now. Three miles they portaged on smooth bear trails around North Pole Rapid, which was so deep and swift they could not attempt it. The mosquitos were beyond belief. Mrs. Hubbard watched them kicking and wriggling and squeezing through the mesh of her head-net close to her eyes. Nothing could keep them out. They went up one's sleeves and pant-legs and down one's neck. Singing, voracious, blood-thirsty clouds surrounded the party whenever they sat down to rest. The men seldom wore head-nets, and Mrs. Hubbard's amazement never ended that they could portage in such pain and not curse or throw off their loads or speak of it. They almost never stopped to eat without lighting smudge fires on all four sides, but even in heavy smoke the mosquitos were in one's eyes and nose and mouth and food, and it was impossible to avoid eating some. Often George flapped a bag around Mrs. Hubbard's head so she could drink her tea.

Her veil proving an insufficient protection, she made herself a mask from a waterproof bag, cutting a large hole in front through which she could see and breathe, and sewing over it several thicknesses of black veilings. Two holes were cut at the back of the ears for ventilation, these also being covered with the veiling. Pulling it over her head, she tied it tight around the neck. It was a fearsome-looking thing, but it kept the flies out. The men said she'd have to take it off when they came to the camps of the Naskapis or the Indians would surely shoot her.

Cold nights brought some relief from the insect torture, but hot nights the whining hordes got into the tents and made sleep almost impossible. The men covered even their heads with blankets and slept half-suffocated—wooly bundles blackened with tens of thousands of angry creatures singing a song of potential death as they crowded each other in their eagerness for blood. The two great realities of life were mosquitos and the fast water flooding endlessly against them, roaring, rushing around islands, tossing its mane, or sliding slick and satiny with irresistible force and a power so endless that human eyes could scarcely look upon those water slopes and keep the courage to go on.

Mrs. Hubbard's admiration for her men continued to grow, they were so considerate of each other, so brave and strong and gay, all bloody and swollen by the clouds of mosquitos. Good days, they were up and portaging at four in the morning. If strength and skill could get her through before the winter closed, that was their pride, something to remember.

Fifteen miles below Seal Lake they left the Naskaupi River's continuous rapids and followed a tributary stream. It was great marten country, Gilbert said, so he called the river *Wapustan*, which is the Montagnais word for marten. Portaging along this stream, they found an ax at Duncan McLean's winter tilt and greeted the find with cheers. Every one of them resolved to guard it, and they said they would carry it with the sugar.

Carrying and paddling for some days, they climbed the hills to a dead stub with a big blaze on it marking a turnoff from the Wapustan toward Seal Lake. July 17 they were in Seal Lake, a beautiful body of water among the hills, with one arm thirty miles long. Seals trapped here by the rising land in geologic ages past had adapted themselves to fresh-water conditions and were frequently seen by trappers. Nineteen miles they paddled that day to a sand-point camp where the upper Naskaupi enters Seal Lake. They were three weeks out from North West River. Next objective: Michikamau!

Mrs. Hubbard was endlessly impressed by the beauty of the skies and waters and the wooded points and islands. "I had none of the feeling of loneliness which I knew everyone would expect me to have. I did not feel far from home, but in reality less homeless than I had ever felt anywhere since I knew my husband was never to come back to me."

Miles above Seal Lake, paddling through a series of lake expansions, they shot a caribou and feasted. The northern lights were very bright that night, drawing away to the northwest in huge and luminous scrolls. Seal Lake had been the limit of Gilbert's knowledge, so he was now carefully scouting the land for new trapping grounds for himself and his brother Donald.

Again they had to leave the river, and the way proved confusing, with chains of lakes and ponds among the valleys, and the need each evening to climb the hills and guess the best way to parallel the river while avoiding its rapids via other ponds and streams.

At the start Mrs. Hubbard felt that her trip was a sacred dedication to her husband's memory, and there is no doubt she undertook it solely for him, expecting nothing but hardship and danger. When she found herself far in the country among the rapids and lakes and hills of that gigantic wilderness, she was overwhelmed and even overjoyed by the grandeur of the land. Somehow the land took her to its heart and began to heal her. And so the quest repaid her in unexpected ways.

She was girlish and poetic, well brought-up, with a certain freshness too. She was always looking for flowers along the portages and noticing any particularly good scenery. Withal she was practical and could mend her boots and cook at the campfire on occasion, and taught herself to take observations for latitude. She understood clearly that such a trip as this must be fast to be successful, because one cannot be certain of game, and lugging quantities of food over the portages is impossible. She stood the flies and the long days extremely well, and was never sick.

She was wise enough to leave the route-picking and the decisions to her guide. If Elson said they could ascend a rapid, they tried it; if he said they must carry, his decisions were never fogged by speculations regarding her preference.

She loved to stand on a rock at the brink of fast rapids looking down at the silky sheen of the swift water, so clear, so bright and full of beauty.

"Mrs. Hubbard, you must not do that," George said.

"Why?"

"You will get dizzy and fall in."

"But I do not get dizzy."

"Maybe you think you will not. It is all right when you are looking at the rapid, but it is when you turn that you will fall. It is very dangerous. If you are going to do that, we will just turn around and go back to North West River."

She said she wouldn't do it any more.

Thereafter, when portaging near heavy rapids the men invented tales of bears and tried to keep her close to them.

It irked her to be so well taken care of, but the men did not like to have her straying off alone looking for berries and flowers. Often there was no time to take her to the hilltop at evening when scouting a portage route.

One afternoon beyond Seal Lake she got permission from George to climb a mountain alone while the men were portaging. "It seemed beautiful to be going off without a guard, and to think of spending an hour or two up on the hilltop quite alone, with the glorious sky above and the beautiful hills and lakes and streams in all directions." She rambled on and on, farther than planned, and when at last she saw a thunderstorm coming and the men far off below in a little cove boiling the billy, she fired two shots to let them know where she was. They began to scramble, they ran. They shouted, firing off rifles. And she went on farther, like a child escaped.

It was a silly, capricious thing to do, and too late she realized it. It was a misunderstanding also, in that seeing them boiling the kettle far below on the lakeshore, she had fired her gun to let them know where she was, so they wouldn't worry. And then when she saw their panic and scrambling pursuit, their conviction it was a distress signal, the recurrent feeling that she was being hedged-about and nursemaided swept over her. And she ran, blindly and instinctively as a rabbit runs. There may have been an element of imagined guilt—that she was free, free and shouldn't be free. Weeks on the trail were behind that unfortunate response, weeks of being shepherded and told she mustn't go alone. Here was she, in an untouched wilderness, financing the trip, unable to go for a stroll without asking her guides, unable to be alone, exploring without being able to explore. Often she and George had laughed about it by the campfires and she had told him what a hard taskmaster he was. She had accepted and known how difficult and necessary it was for George to be assured always of her safety. But now she ran, and it is doubtful if she herself knew why. Soon she stopped, and there they caught her. They were dripping with sweat, hands shaking, eyes wild with apprehension.

The meeting was a tangle of embarrassment, relief, antagonism and remorse impossible to describe. They did not know themselves what elemental chords had been touched. But, for George, in his characteristically bighearted way, relief predominated.

She and George had the only sharp words of the trip. He told her she never could go away alone again. "Who would ever think to see you and the little short steps that you could go away there, and so quick too," he said. "I thought I was never going to see you again. What would we do if you got lost or fell in that rapid? I could never go back again. How could any of us go back without you?"

George's already-great sense of responsibility had been sharpened by the Hubbard tragedy. The fact that he had been obliged to go for rescue did not for him change the fact that he lived and Hubbard died.

The atmosphere was decidedly strained in camp that night. She loaned the men the expedition's one bottle of brandy so they could have a small bracer. Instead, they drank it almost dry.

At last they stood on a hill and saw the great shining Michikamau. George pointed out to her only a few miles away the lofty land he called Mount Hubbard, where he and Hubbard had stood two years before and seen the lake. He pointed out Windbound Lake and the blind-alley necklace through which he and Hubbard had hoped to proceed. He showed her the hill far away where he had shot a rabbit, and another where he got a partridge in the long-ago starvation time.

That night they had rice pudding for dessert, in celebration of their nearness to Michikamau. But it was more than another day's hard travel, with more portages and confused, rapid, tortuous streams before they finally entered the lake. All this while they had kept track of the Naskaupi River, frequently far from its rapids and falls but always paralleling its direction. Now they were camped on an island, weary and late, in Michikamau near the spot where the river left the lake. It was a beautiful island flower garden, an Indian campground with many old wigwam poles and the shavings curled from their crooked-knives where they had made canoe ribs and snowshoe frames. Hung on bushes, swinging in the wind, were the little packets of bones to placate the spirits of other rabbits and other caribou so that there might always be more and never a starving time. Gilbert cooked up rice pudding dessert for them again that night, on the basis that the earlier celebration had been premature.

Being near the spot where Naskaupi waters flow out of the lake, they were at a focal point. Before they shoved off on the broad waters next day, Mrs. Hubbard had Job blaze two trees at the shore and wrote with a flint on a big flat rock, HUBBARD EXPEDITION ARRIVED HERE AUGUST 2ND 1905. No one will ever know whether it was a monument to Leonidas, a record in case they should perish further on, or a signboard she hoped Wallace would see as he struggled in her wake. Perhaps a little of all three.

All day they paddled. Only a little trolling brought a fifteen-pound *naymaycush*, which they cooked for lunch on an island. A headwind came, and the canoes dipped water in the great rolling troughs, but evening calmed the waters so that far away they could see floating ice and many islands. Out on the glittering water a loon called; and another wild call answered. Mrs. Hubbard knew how lucky she was to be afloat on that great lake of dreams, ninety-five miles long and twenty-six wide—the first woman of her race to see it since time began. The sun went down on the huge shining lake with its distant blue islands and left the two little canoes rocking in the long northern twilight, with the loons still crying. All night they heard the waves roll on the beach.

In a fine fair wind they put up little sails and soared all day. After rapids and carries and flies, this was magic, a picnic, a luxury. And again next day they sailed and sailed, till a storm threatened, bringing big waves rolling up the huge expanse. The water was dark blue and raked with whitecaps; the sky was dark. They had an hour's hard fight there, turned against the wind, to cross a wide bay and reach the lakehead. If they did not gain a lee, they might be stormbound for days. The men grew silent and determined. George twisted the canoe a little toward each wave to avoid shipping water. Sitting amidships, with her hands on the gunnels, Mrs. Hubbard felt the water running up her sleeves as the canoe dipped. Round the last point the men bent the paddles with all the strength in their arms, pushing the tossed canoes through the last breakers and into a quiet bay beyond.

That afternoon they ascended a short shallow stream into Lake Michikamats, twenty-five miles long, "The Little Bigwater," and scudded again at racing pace before a heavy south wind. At nightfall they pitched their camp on the ridge of a lovely island among spruce trees, with moss and a carpet of boughs, and a fine breeze that drove away the flies. Here they were windbound for two days, two blessed days of rest, with leisure for a bath. George shot a caribou, two geese and a partridge, so they lived high. Indians had found this ideal spot too, and there were many remains of old camps, with well-worn paths leading from one to the other. It was strange to think that here in the midst of loneliness so vast it had killed her husband was a crossroads, homey and familiar to a wilderness people, with their cooking fires and tent places and the pegs between which they swung their babies in little hammocks.

When, at the end of the gale, Mrs. Hubbard's party loaded up and launched out again, they soon came to an Indian graveyard on a sand mound overlooking a bay. Each grave was surrounded by a small wooden paling, as the Montagnais do, and all were old and weathered except one, a child's. Fresh shavings spoke of an Indian who had fashioned this place for his child above the shining blue lake.

At the end of Michikamats was a two-mile marsh and brooks, ponds, a one-mile lake, a stream feeding it, an Indian trail, another one-mile lake, and at last no inlet at the head of the lake. They had reached the source of the Naskaupi, they were on the divide between Atlantic and Arctic waters, and the divide was a bog. Then they were over, scouting an outlet to their lake for the first time, rather than an inlet. It was August 11 and they were on the George River, on the north-flowing waters. At first it was only a tiny stream hidden in a rocky bed among willows. Soon it would swell to a mighty waterway.

A week of snow and rain hit them. They had three hundred miles to go. Careening down rapids joining a series of lake expansions, they were looking for the Indian villages of the upper George, the nomad Indians whose life is the caribou. Gilbert was telling them about the tall Naskapis and their white deerskin clothes, Gilbert who was fond of Indians all his life and already knew their language.

"We are strangers passing through your country," shouted George each time as they paddled into a village, one a Montagnais, the other a Naskapi. Most of the men were away. The women wanted a present of Mrs. Hubbard's green sweater. "Of course you have some tobacco," the women said, bringing out their pipes. And George and Gilbert replied in their language, "Only a little. We have come far."

The Indian women thought it most strange that Mrs. Hubbard did not smoke a pipe, she coming from the land of tobacco. Tobacco came from Englishmen, and she was an Englishman's woman, obviously.

Down Indian House Lake the party pushed. Job had a dream of dangerous falls and rapids, perhaps inspired by the Indians' description of the river. They slid down the strange river warily, with an extra paddle close at hand should one be broken. Sure enough, there followed five days of almost continuous rapids, with the river ahead a wild slope of foam, and the steersman standing whenever he could in the pitching canoe to peer out a course. "Slanting Lake" tipped not only from end to end but from one side to the other with the force of the current. Dropping down this boiling black flood in a deathlike silence gave them a sense of being surrounded by treachery. Swifter and swifter they flew down the glittering river that wound through a jumble of mountains, until the strain grew so tense they ran ashore to rest.

Years later, when Gilbert Blake had become a middle-aged man and possessed more first-hand knowledge of interior Labrador than any other living traveler, he often spoke with joy of the fearsome rapids on the George River. His eyes crinkled with the same boyish gaiety they must have had at evening making camp beside that great stream: "The shores was all clifty and we couldn't get out, so day on day we run 'em and just let 'er rip. You don't know where she's goin' but you're goin' to follow 'er *whatever!* There's nothin' for me like frosty mornings in new country and the river opening up ahead and the big hills closin' in behind." All through his adventurous life he continued making canoe journeys into the Labrador bush with prospectors and mapmakers, sometimes as much as eight hundred miles in a summer. But of all his expeditions he most prized the one with Mrs. Hubbard.

When she was walking beside an extra-bad rapid, Mrs. Hubbard found boulders sixty feet above the water, tossed there by spring ice. Here George and Job were whirled around and banged against a cliff, crawled out on a shelf and launched again. The country was like Norwegian fiords. Behind them the mountains stood on either side like giant forts, and George, glancing back, said with awe, "Looks like we just got out of prison." Still the river roared down its narrow valley, swollen by huge tributaries that entered on either hand. At one point where it dropped by a series of wild cascades and then by almost equally wild rapids, they had to leave it for a one-and-a-quarter-mile carry. At the portage end was a lake expansion into which the river shot with such force as to make a raised ridge of foam and water far out into the lake. And still the river flowed in rapids till they looked at each other and asked, "Will it never end?"

On the Cree Indian, Job, fell the heavy responsibility of choosing the pathway through these torrents or saying they must stop and reconnoiter. When the light was bad in the setting sun, he went ashore to scout ahead. But that took time. Seldom they paused, making sometimes sixty miles a day. Hour after hour he looked into the maelstrom, studying the lines in the face of fury, choosing, choosing. In all this time, Job as steersman and George as bow paddle in the lead canoe, with Mrs. Hubbard amidships, showed themselves superb canoemen. As they plunged over the lip of a thundering chute, Mrs. Hubbard, weary from the daily danger and the mosquito-filled nights, had difficulty relaxing to let her bodyweight swing with the canoe; but she knew she must, and tried hard not to grip the gunnels. Gilbert and Joseph followed where they led, and watched them narrowly to see how they fared. Often Job would stand and shout above the noise as he took them far out into the surges to dodge breaking boulders close ashore. Though the strain of it day after day finally made him actually ill, he never faltered and never made that wrong, split-second decision that would have finished them.

The river was two miles wide, and still they came to another rapid so rough it twisted George and Job stern-to as it shot them into its maw. But they turned in their places and ran it stern first anyway. It was the last one. They had come to the sea tides and salt water.

On a calm Sabbath morning they pulled in to the post near the mouth of the George, by the shores of Ungava, a tiny group of white buildings with red roofs looking microscopic at the foot of a huge mountain of solid rock. They were greeted by Mr. Ford, the HBC agent. The supply steamer had not come yet. Mrs. Ford, a blue-eyed woman waiting at the hill below her house, clasped Mrs. Hubbard and said, "You are very welcome. Yours is the first white woman's face I have seen in two years."

Happy in the warmth of the welcome, overwhelmed at the realization of success and arrival, Mrs. Hubbard hurried up to the house with Mrs. Ford. And then she looked down and saw her men still sitting in the canoe. Why weren't they coming up the hill too? Suddenly she remembered this was "civilization," this was a British post, with the traditions of the empire. She had forgotten that arrival at the post would reverse their positions. Remorse flooded her that she had not realized they were her charges now, as she had been their charge before. Through all the long journey they had brought her unharmed, with kindness, gentleness and true chivalry. Her heart smote her to think she had left them without a word.

She turned and ran down the hill to them, crossed the mud of the tidal flat, and one by one took their hands in hers. Tears filled her eyes as she thanked them with the deepest sense of gratitude and humility for all they had done, so much more than she could ever repay.

She brought them up to the house with her, and since it was small she did the best she could and saw to it that they had a good camping place among the willows. It gave her a feeling of loneliness to see the tents go up and know that she would not again be part of that encampment. As Gilbert used to say twenty-five years later, "She were a true lady, Mrs. Hubbard, and less trouble than most men."

That night her thoughts were all of Hubbard and of the unusually bad season of rain and cold he had experienced; of the maps that had led him astray; and his bravery in the face of defeat and death. Lacking him, it seemed very little that she had accomplished. But she had done what she could.

It was August 27. Her party had covered 567 miles in 61 days, of which 43 were spent traveling and 18 in camps. She had started with 750 pounds of food, and arrived with 150 pounds surplus. She had finished the job her husband began.

PART 3

All this time Wallace was struggling across the country many weeks behind. He did not follow up the Naskaupi so far as Mrs. Hubbard, but turned off some dozen miles above Grand Lake opposite the Red Wine River, and began to portage across the lakes and hills. In *The Long Labrador Trail* he said he did this purposely because he wanted to follow "the old Indian route." Duncan McLean, one of the Susan's Brook rescuers, who was accompanying the party, told Wallace the route was not a good one. To this Wallace replied, "We are not on a summer picnic," and took off on the dim and over-grown trail. Two years before, the finding of smooth rocks on which Indians had built their winter fires along the untraversable Susan had led nowhere but to Hubbard's death. Yet then as now Wallace hailed with joy each old campsite as an indication of the true route. Whites, busily journeying from one specific destination to another, often find it impossible to appreciate the fact that the country is home to the Indians, and they are not necessarily going anywhere. The nomads are merely seeking food wherever it occurs, and never imagined their trail crossings and figure 8's would be made into a fiction writer's highway to success. Wallace had no flair for reading Indian minds or making friends with "natives." His story, this time as always, was one of hardships bravely endured; and there is no doubt he showed great fortitude in steadfastly carrying on across long, steep portages that had to be chopped out, groping among ponds, rapids, brooks, looking always for Indian signs and sometimes finding tepee poles a hundred years old that crumbled at the touch.

The five men with Wallace were: George Richards, a geologist from Columbia University, New York City; Clifford H. Eaton, also of New York City; Leigh Stanton, a veteran of the Boer War; Peter Stevens, an Ojibwa Indian of Grand Marais, Minnesota, who served as hunter and camp servant; and Duncan McLean, who went back home to North West River a little before they reached

Lake Nepishish. At sunset evening after evening they trudged three or four miles farther to climb a hill and study a way ahead among the bogs and streams.

Each carry meant two trips, so that every five-mile advance cost a fifteen-mile tramp, of which ten were done with packs on their backs. Tumplines rubbed their ears and flies ate them alive. Day after day and week after week the toil went on, climbing hills, sinking in swamps, hauling through rapids, and ferrying across ponds so small it hardly paid to load the canoe for the crossing.

Rainy nights they did have the blessing this time of a tin stove and pipe for their tent—items of equipment no trapper would be without, for in cold wet times the combination makes a comfortable home most anywhere.

Wallace was fishing in a rapid one day, when he slipped off a rock head over ears into the water. Pete the Indian laughed at him. Wallace wrote in his journal, "I could see no occasion for his hilarity and told him so."

They struck Crooked River, a tributary of the Naskaupi which is almost one continuous rapid. Then came a welcome respite paddling up Lake Nepishish. Beyond were strings of lakes lost among rolling hills. Sometimes from their vantage point they could count fifty lakes or more.

Leaving Seal Lake by the Naskaupi River as Mrs. Hubbard had done, they branched off some distance to the north on an eleven-mile carry that took two days in rain and gusts of wind so strong two men had to carry each canoe. Thus they had to make three loads of each stage, which meant fifty-five miles actual walking for the eleven-mile gain, thirty-three miles of this distance with packs. Soon all sign of Indian camps, even the most ancient, petered out and they were left to fight their way to Michikamau as best they could through a country desolated by forest fires and devoid of fish or game. Sleet and rain were pelting them. It was now August 23.

As they progressed, they encountered quantities of owls and shot as many as six a day, all of which went into the pot to conserve the dwindling food supply. Portaging over ridges, they came to a hill four hundred feet high from whose top they could look away for fifty miles across a network of lakes set in country as level as a table. But no Michikamau.

It was September 3, and summer was over when they finished another of those innumerable half-mile portages, broke through the brush and laid their canoes down on the sandy shore of Michikamau. They were several miles north of the point where Naskaupi River leaves the lake, so it is doubtful they saw Mrs. Hubbard's flint-marked rock and double blaze. In any case this camp on the shore of the Great Lake of the Indians was their last together as a group.

As he approached Michikamau, Wallace had been explaining to his men that food was getting short and the season late. He told them he could not be sure of getting to Ungava in time to catch the once-a-year supply steamer out; neither could he expect to winter them all there. He and a companion would go on. Three would have to go back. After due deliberation, he chose Clifford Eaton, the young man from Manhattan, to accompany him.

Having fought a way almost to the height of land, the other three, Peter Stevens, George Richards, and Leigh Stanton, were sad indeed to discover they were only a support party who must now go back. They had enlisted for Ungava; the turning back was hard to bear. Stevens repeatedly beseeched Wallace to take him as the chosen companion. He was the guide, he said, and how could he ever reappear in civilized places if two of the party were lost in the bush, as seemed quite likely. As a matter of fact, he had done more than his share with pole, paddle, and tracking line, as well as lugging big loads through the fly-infested brush. He had been especially useful in scouting out a way through the mazes of ponds, lakes, and streams. In addition, he had expertly done all the camp cooking for the party of five.

Wallace found it hard to withstand the Indian's pleadings but told Stevens he must return in order to see the other, less-experienced woodsmen safely out.

Fine men all, they drowned their disappointment in generosity, contributing boots, a shirt, the tent and stove, and most of their tobacco. They gave Wallace and Eaton a majority of the food, taking for themselves but the barest minimum to keep themselves alive on the long hard return journey to North West River—a journey that as a matter of fact involved more portages, more repeated toil, and perhaps more difficulty than the one Wallace faced.

Richards took a picture of Wallace and Eaton launched on the lake in their canoe, which Wallace in the fulsome style of his book later used with the caption, "Our lonely perilous journey toward the dismal wastes was begun." The advance waved farewell to the three who were making their advance possible, and so the party split. It says much for the competence of the returnees that they reached North West River safely and caught the last steamer south before ice closed the coast.

Paddling hard up Michikamau, racing against the coming winter, Wallace and Eaton were extremely fortunate not to be windbound by the hurricane gales that regularly sweep the Labrador peninsula in the fall. The day they hit the headwaters of the George, they were a full month behind Mrs. Hubbard and had heavy snow. Pressing on as fast as he could, Wallace spent little time at the two Indian villages where Mrs. Hubbard had stopped. Yet beyond there he shot two caribou and stayed in camp four days fixing the meat and preparing a cache in case he should "have to retreat to it." This was extremely odd, for though he had not seen the lower George rapids, the Indians could have told him no one has ever retreated up its gorges. The explanation is, probably, that neither he nor Eaton could speak or understand the Indian language.

September 28, a driving snowstorm and gale so bitter it froze spray on the rocks held them ashore. Wallace's situation was not so different now from that of two years before. Again he was wandering far too late on the height of land, grub short, clothing worn, uncertain whether he would be one more canoe-and-portage traveler claimed by winter. September 29, despite the gale and freezing spray, they had to go. The canoe was soon weighted with ice and the paddles were heavy with it. A half a foot of snow lay on the ground. Going down a strip of white water in the cold, they hit a rock and like a flash capsized. Wallace rolled down through the rocks of the icy rapid. Eaton clung to the capsized canoe. In quiet water below, they got ashore, where they found that the lighter bags and paddles were floating away; everything heavy had sunk beyond hope of recovery. Bitterly they blamed themselves that they had not tied in their gear. The thwarts, however, had held fast in the canoe a bag of pemmican, one other small bag, the tent, and the tent stove.

Blue and numb, knowing they would soon perish with cold, they looked about for wood. There was none. The nearest driftwood was an eighth of a mile across a bay. The paddles were gone, but they embarked and paddled across with their stiff hands. Eaton pulled down wood. Though Wallace's hands were like clubs, he succeeded in squeezing his waterproof matches out of his pocket and getting a match between his stiff fingers. All the rocks were covered with snow. When he struck several matches on the bottom of the wet box, the heads flew off. The two men were dying before their own eyes. In desperation they tried to run to restore circulation, but their legs would not obey them, and they fell flat among the rocks and snow. Wallace made one last-ditch attempt with the matches, holding them between his hands with the aid of his eyes, for he could not feel them. One by one the matches failed or went out until only three were left. One of them fell into the snow, leaving two. This next-to-last match caught alight in a handful of hairy moss from the trunk of a spruce tree; he nursed the sticks to a roaring blaze.

Stripping off their frozen clothes, they stood in their underwear in the snow before the life-giving fire. Dried and clothed again, they sat by the warm blaze and had a smoke from their toasted plug of tobacco, which Wallace later said was the best smoke he ever had in his life. With joy and surprise they found in an eddy below not only their paddles but dunnage bags containing blankets and clothes. Guns, all axes, the stovepipe, balance of provisions, and all cooking utensils were gone. There still remained matches in a bag, fifty pounds of pemmican, tea, and five or six pounds of caribou tallow.

Next day they were portaging around falls and running wild rapids again. Nights were ordeals of suffering, now that there was no ax, no stovepipe, and no chance to warm the tent. But one freezing night at the head of Indian House Lake they found some old rusty stovepipe abandoned by an Indian. And each night thereafter, by breaking branches with their hands, they had a fire in their tent stove. Tributaries were joining the deepening, rushing river. Hearing the roar of rapids five or six miles ahead, they skirted monstrous cross-current rips that would have swallowed them like a chip. Caught in this wintry desolation and thunder, they spoke scarcely a dozen words in a day. Blue landmarks looming ahead soon dropped astern and disappeared as the two half-frozen men sped down the rock-walled gorges.

At last they saw their destination, the George River Post, across a vast mudflat left by a forty-foot ebb tide, and, abandoning their canoe and gear on a rise, they tried to walk to it along the side of a cliff above the mud. But darkness caught them among the precipitous rocks, where they sat hungrily watching the cozy flicker of distant lighted windows. Here was the end of their six-hundred-mile seeking—those diminutive buildings on the immense northern shore—and here they sat, making a fire and hoping to be seen.

At length Wallace was rescued again when an Eskimo in a boat took them off their perch to the Post, where they were welcomed by Mr. Ford. It was October 16, a time of year when full winter has arrived on that severe arctic coast facing the polar blasts, a time of year when no summer canoe traveler can reasonably expect to get out of the bush alive. The portage lakes were frozen; only the fact that he was on a strong-flowing river had given Wallace open water to travel on.

Speaking of a chat that first night and the "interesting things" he had to tell post manager Ford, Wallace says "Over a year had passed since his last communication with the outside world." But Mrs. Hubbard had been there more than a month, and had certainly brought some news of the outside world. You would not guess this truth from the pages of *The Long Labrador Trail*. You would not guess she was there at all.

In his book describing the journey, Wallace takes pains to imply that he is the first to make the long canoe-and-portage crossing, and that it is he who has completed the work Hubbard died trying to accomplish. Several times in the book he casts himself in the role of Hubbard's spiritual savior, a man dedicated to his friend's memory and risking his life for the sake of that friend who died in the tent beside the Susan.

At the crowded little George River Post, the atmosphere between Wallace and Mrs. Hubbard was strained, to say the least. She had been there a month and a half, waiting for the steamer. But in the account of her expedition she does not speak of Wallace's arrival. Though Wallace must have seen many signs of her camping places, you would never suspect from his story that the great brooding wilderness was crossed by two parties in the summer of 1905.

It is interesting to speculate on the contrasting aspects of these omissions. Had she told of him, she could scarcely have avoided saying that she had arrived at the George River post six weeks ahead, in a more successful journey. If he had spoken of her, he'd have difficulty explaining his lateness, his turned-back support party, and his many mistakes. In other words, her silence appears generous, his ungenerous.

Mr. Ford was extremely worried by the nonarrival of the supply steamer *Pelican*. Perhaps she had been wrecked and lost, perhaps it would be another year before he saw a ship. Though he was even now a year without supplies and scraping the bottoms of barrels, here were seven extra mouths to feed somehow over a ten-month winter. He had no way of knowing that the *Pelican* had indeed torn off her keel on a reef and had to limp south to a drydock for repairs, but that her do-or-die skipper was now on the way.

October 19, the long-delayed ship came in, and Mr. Ford's heart must have lifted as the red HBC flag went up and the shotguns boomed their traditional welcome to the men coming in from the outer world. It was a great moment at the northern posts. Mrs. Hubbard and her guides embarked for home. But Wallace refused. Wishing to see Fort Chimo Post, 125 miles west along the shore of Ungava Bay, he set off with Eaton in the small boat of several Eskimos who were reluctant to take him. Mr. Ford earnestly begged Wallace not to go, telling him that it was suicide and that the season for small-boat travel on that coast was long past. Wallace's opinion that too many post managers are too cautious was soon changed by a blizzard, during which the boat was forced ashore by ice. Starved and frozen for days, the travelers at length staggered by luck into a broken cabin. Here the Eskimos left the two whites, who could not take another step, and went on another two days through the blinding storm, still without food (an incredible feat), to Whale River Post. The post sent two fine strong dog teams racing, and after five days in the cabin without food Wallace was once again rescued. Late that winter he hired dog teams and local guides to take himself and Eaton from post to post and from settlement to settlement south around the coast all the way from Chimo to the Gulf of St. Lawrence.

On this long journey his Eskimo or settler teamsters drove the dogs, provided the sledge, dog food, and usually the people food. Along the Ungava barrens they made the igloo, or in wooded country farther south the camp, finding the way even in blizzards among mountains or across sea ice, while he followed the portages, bays, and coastal routes where they took him. His clothing and boots were sewn by north coast women, and he was fed, warmed, and restored at lonely Hudson's Bay Company posts and the Moravian stations along both the wild Ungava and Atlantic coasts. He says his trek covered two thousand miles. In any case, it was made possible by the supplies, knowledge, and abilities of some fifty, sixty, or perhaps seventy generous people, some of whom were short of food when he arrived and shorter when he and Eaton left.

Mrs. Hubbard sailed away from the solid-rock shores of Ungava with memories of her husband in her heart. She wished it could have been he who crossed all those hundreds of miles of lakes and rivers. She saw to it that her guides went safely back to their native villages, and returned to her own home near New York. In 1908, the McClure Company issued her book, *A Woman's Way through Unknown Labrador.* She closed her pages with a tribute to her husband and his bravery alone in the tent, and asked if she had accomplished anything that it be considered a monument to him.

Wallace's *The Long Labrador Trail* achieved much greater fame than Mrs. Hubbard's book. It went into many, many editions. Wallace had a facility for exploiting the story-telling elements of his risks and hardships. In the United States in the early 1900s Dillon Wallace became widely known and acclaimed as a great wilderness traveler, woodsman, and explorer. George Elson was not so well known. Nevertheless, Elson's magnificent achievement, though he had the least of the precious flour, in getting out alive and promptly sending back a rescue team will always remain in distinct contrast to Wallace's effort. The fact that Wallace's journeys were near-tragedies did not dim his fame.

So ends the saga of three expeditions and the four erstwhile friends, Leonidas Hubbard, Dillon Wallace, George Elson, and Mina Hubbard. Perhaps the kernel of the story is not in the three books at all but in the guides, those men of Indian, Eskimo, Scottish, and French admixture who find the way and give their loyalty. These are the men who carry the loads. In a black night of wind on a wild shore, they are not dismayed. They seldom write of bad-ice rapids or the lonely campfire in the snow—nor of the leaders they have led home.

It is now more than eighty years since that eventful summer, and to the best of my knowledge no canoe-and-portage party has in one season made the long crossing between North West River and George River Post from that day to this.

The Long Crossing and Other Labrador Stories
was designed and composed in 10.5/14 Utopia on a
Macintosh FX by Octavo Design & Production, La Jolla, California;
printed by Braun-Brumfield, Ann Arbor, Michigan;
and published by
The University of Maine Press
Orono, Maine 04469